CHARTWORK Charts are overprinted with a lattice of latitude and longitude

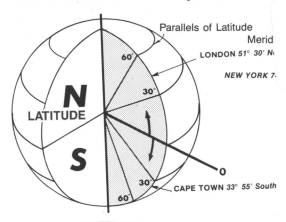

Parallels of Latitude

Meridians...

LONDON 51° 30′ No...

NEW YORK 7...

LATITUDE

N

S

60°

30°

30°

60°

0

CAPE TOWN 33° 55′ South

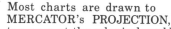

W E

LONGITUDE

30° 15′ 0° 15′ 30°

GREENWICH MERIDIAN

CAPE TOWN 18° 22′ East

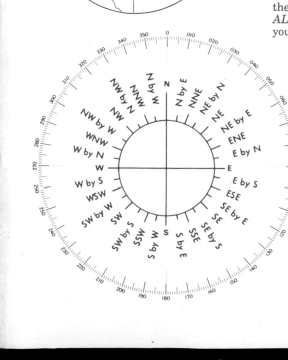

Most charts are drawn to
MERCATOR's PROJECTION,
to represent the spherical world on a flat sheet of
paper with all the meridians of longitude made
parallel. To keep the same land shapes the parallels
of Latitude are increased in proportion.

This gives rise to say **600 seamiles** being measured
on a chart being a bigger measurement at the top
of the chart than at the bottom.

This is because **1 seamile = 1 minute of latitude**
and the latitude scale gradually increases towards
the top of the chart. *This is why distances are
ALWAYS* measured on the latitude scale opposite
your position.

DIRECTION is always
measured from North in a
three figure notation **000°**
(North) **090°** (East), **180°**
(South) **270°** (West) to **359°**.

WIND DIRECTION is
usually in the form of points
of the compass ie. **N, NNE,
NE by N** etc.

INFORMATION ON ADMIRALTY CHARTS

(A) Chart 'CATALOGUE NUMBER' **(B)** 'TITLE' describes area covered.

(C) 'DEPTH' units of measurement — mostly metric but still some old (fathom 6ft) charts around.

(D) 'SCALE' 1 unit of distance on chart = (in this case) 20,000 units on the earth's surface.

(E) Other important information is given a prominent place on the chart.

(F) TIDAL INFORMATION is given as a true bearing and speed in knots (see page 23)

(G) The annual change in MAGNETIC VARIATION is shown on the compass rose (see page 10)

(H) The LATITUDE SCALE on each side is used for measuring distance in Nautical Miles.

(I) The LONGITUDE SCALE at the top and bottom is for position only and *NOT* for measuring distance.

(J) LAND is shown as beige. **(K)** DRYING AREA green **(L)** INSHORE WATERS are normally blue.

(M) The 'EDITION DATE' lets you check with a chart list to see if its the latest edition. (Although a 1980 edition might still be the latest edition in 1990 if nothing has changed).

(N) SMALL CORRECTIONS (such as buoys moving) can be made by yourself or a chart agent. Corrections are published in 'Notice to Mariners' and their numbers noted on the chart.

IT IS VERY IMPORTANT TO KEEP YOUR CHARTS UP TO DATE.

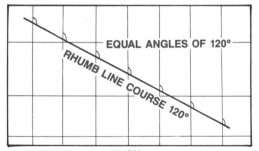

MERCATOR PROJECTION

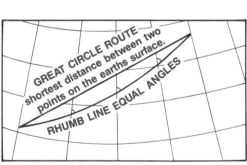

GNOMONIC PROJECTION

MERCATOR PROJECTION (see page 1) has the meridians of Longitude and the parallels of Latitude drawn in a rectangular grid pattern. So, a course crosses the grid at equal angles. This is known as a RHUMB LINE.

GNOMONIC PROJECTION has converging straight meridians and curved parallels of latitude. It is used in Polar regions, large oceans and small harbour plans. Ships can follow a Great Circle Route to save fuel.

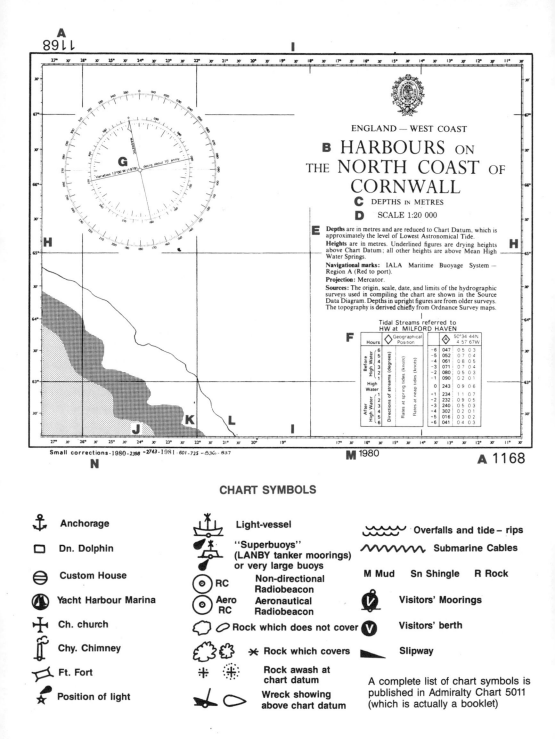

A 1168

ENGLAND — WEST COAST

B **HARBOURS** ON THE **NORTH COAST** OF **CORNWALL**

C DEPTHS IN METRES

D SCALE 1:20 000

E **Depths** are in metres and are reduced to Chart Datum, which is approximately the level of Lowest Astronomical Tide.

Heights are in metres. Underlined figures are drying heights above Chart Datum; all other heights are above Mean High Water Springs.

Navigational marks: IALA Maritime Buoyage System — Region A (Red to port).

Projection: Mercator.

Sources: The origin, scale, date, and limits of the hydrographic surveys used in compiling the chart are shown in the Source Data Diagram. Depths in upright figures are from older surveys. The topography is derived chiefly from Ordnance Survey maps.

Tidal Streams referred to
HW at MILFORD HAVEN

F

	Hours	Geographical Position		50°34·44N 4 57 67W		
		◇	Directions of streams (degrees)	◇	Rates at spring tides (knots)	Rates at neap tides (knots)
Before High Water	-6	047			0·5	0·3
	-5	052			0·7	0·4
	-4	061			0·8	0·5
	-3	071			0·7	0·4
	-2	080			0·5	0·3
	-1	090			0·2	0·1
High Water	0	243			0·9	0·6
After High Water	+1	234			1·1	0·7
	+2	232			0·9	0·5
	+3	240			0·5	0·3
	+4	302			0·2	0·1
	+5	016			0·3	0·2
	+6	041			0·4	0·3

Variation 12°00′W (1979) decrg about 10′ annly

MAGNETIC

Small corrections—1980-2398 -2743-1981-601-725 -836-837

N

M 1980

A 1168

CHART SYMBOLS

⚓ Anchorage

▢ Dn. Dolphin

⊖ Custom House

Yacht Harbour Marina

⌖ Ch. church

Chy. Chimney

Ft. Fort

Position of light

Light-vessel

"Superbuoys"
(LANBY tanker moorings)
or very large buoys

⊙ RC Non-directional Radiobeacon

⊙ Aero RC Aeronautical Radiobeacon

Rock which does not cover

Rock which covers

Rock awash at chart datum

Wreck showing above chart datum

Overfalls and tide – rips

Submarine Cables

M Mud   Sn Shingle   R Rock

Visitors' Moorings

Visitors' berth

Slipway

A complete list of chart symbols is published in Admiralty Chart 5011 (which is actually a booklet)

3

PLOTTING A POSITION

A position on the earth's surface can be plotted in two ways:-

LATITUDE AND LONGITUDE say,
Latitude 45° 02' North by Longitude 5° 54' West
With a suitable instrument (see page 40) draw a line from 45° 02'N on the Latitude scale *up the side of the chart.*
Then mark off the position of 5° 54'W of Longitude.
One way to do this is to set your dividers from the nearest meridian to the position on the longitude scale *(top and bottom)* and transfer it to the 45° 02'N parallel.

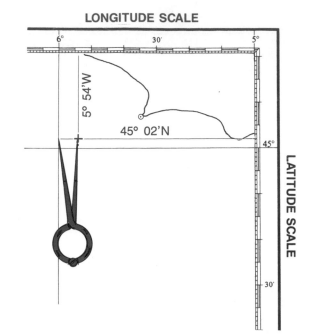

The other way of plotting a position is with a BEARING AND DISTANCE from a charted place.
Draw a line at the given bearing say 250° True from the charted place.
Transfer the bearing from the compass rose printed on the chart or use a suitable protractor
Then measure 15 minutes of latitude which equals 15 miles.
IT IS VERY IMPORTANT TO MEASURE FROM THE SCALE OPPOSITE YOUR POSITION
Step off the distance down your bearing line.

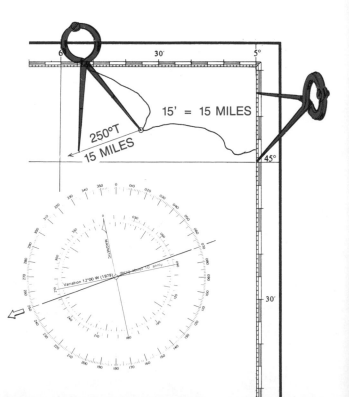

CHARTWORK

The instruments needed for chartwork are simply a soft pencil (2B), so you can rub out the lines easily, a pair of dividers to transfer measurements, and some means of measuring or transferring an angle.

Pencil and Dividers

A modern 'reloadable' pencil, saves a lot of mess and frustration when the sharpener goes missing! And a pair of brass dividers can be used single handed.

Parallel Rule

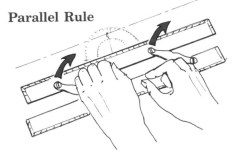

Breton Plotter

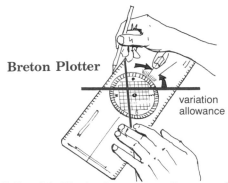

variation allowance

Rolling Rule

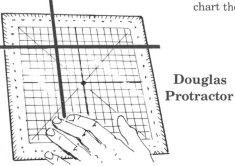

'Parallel' and 'rolling' rules can transfer an angle from the printed compass rose, by "walking" or rolling across the chart.

Rolling rules are good on dining room tables — almost useless on a yacht.

In rough conditions it is often easier to use a protractor of some sort. The Douglas protractor grid can be alined with the chart and the angle measured off. If working in "magnetic" you must make allowance for variation. With the 'Breton' and 'Hurst' plotters the protractor can be pre-set for variation.

This means when the grids are aligned with the chart the bearings read off are already in magnetic.

Hurst Plotter

variation allowance

Douglas Protractor

THE COURSE is the way we want to go and when related to the compass it is the **COURSE TO STEER.**

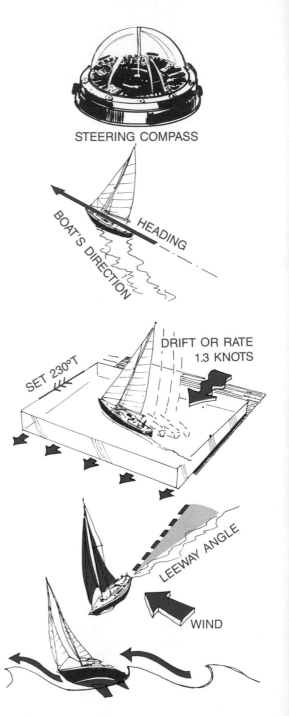

STEERING COMPASS

THE HEADING is the way the boat is pointing, ideally this should be the same as the course. If not, the helmsman must note in the log the course actually steered.

Note the boat is moving through the water in a different direction from the heading this is due LEEWAY.

HEADING

BOAT'S DIRECTION

TIDAL SET AND DRIFT
SET is the direction the tide is going and **DRIFT** is the distance the water has moved in a period of time.
(If the water has drifted say 1.3 miles in 1 hour it's called a RATE of 1.3 KNOTS).

Symbol to draw on chart

DRIFT OR RATE
1.3 KNOTS

SET 230°T

LEEWAY is how much we are blown sideways by the wind. Measuring the bearing of the wake and comparing it with the reciprocal of the **HEADING** gives us a clue. But this is only possible in calm conditions and most people estimate say 3°5° based on past experience.
In rough condition 10°20° of LEEWAY is possible as the boat can be bodily moved sideways.

LEEWAY ANGLE

WIND

WATER TRACK is the path we make through the water (ie the wake) allowing to leeway.

Symbol to draw on chart

→

GROUND TRACK is the actual path we make over the sea bed.

Symbol to draw on chart

→→

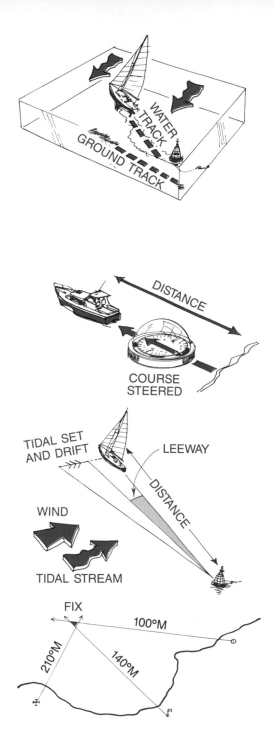

DEAD RECKONING (D.R.) is a position deduced from a course steered and a distance run. *It makes no allowance for tidal set and drift or leeway* so is of little practical use in coastal navigation.

ESTIMATED POSITION (E.P.) is the best possible estimate of a present or future position. It is based on a distance run from a known position *with an allowance made for both leeway and the tidal set and drift.*

Symbol △

A FIX is when we know where we are by using compass, radio direction bearings, depth soundings, transits or one of the many electronic aids to navigation available now.

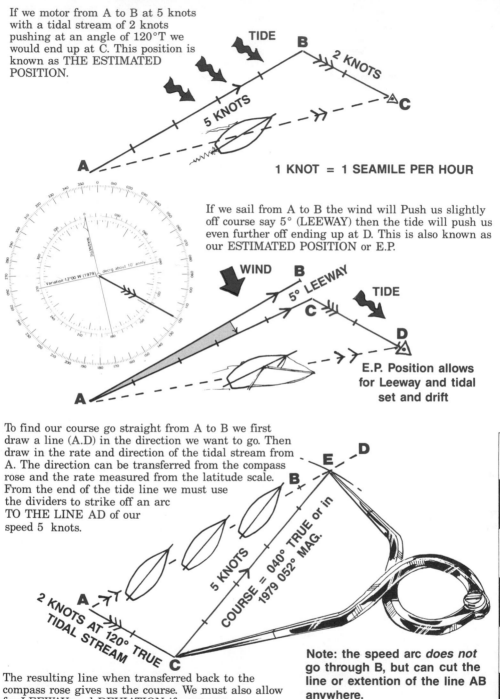

If we motor from A to B at 5 knots with a tidal stream of 2 knots pushing at an angle of 120°T we would end up at C. This position is known as THE ESTIMATED POSITION.

TIDE

B

2 KNOTS

C

5 KNOTS

A

1 KNOT = 1 SEAMILE PER HOUR

If we sail from A to B the wind will Push us slightly off course say 5° (LEEWAY) then the tide will push us even further off ending up at D. This is also known as our ESTIMATED POSITION or E.P.

WIND **B** **LEEWAY**

5° LEEWAY **TIDE**

C

D

A

E.P. Position allows for Leeway and tidal set and drift

To find our course go straight from A to B we first draw a line (A.D) in the direction we want to go. Then draw in the rate and direction of the tidal stream from A. The direction can be transferred from the compass rose and the rate measured from the latitude scale. From the end of the tide line we must use the dividers to strike off an arc TO THE LINE AD of our speed 5 knots.

E **D**

B

5 KNOTS

COURSE = 040° TRUE or in 1979 052° MAG.

A

2 KNOTS AT 120° TRUE TIDAL STREAM

C

The resulting line when transferred back to the compass rose gives us the course. We must also allow for LEEWAY and DEVIATION if necessary.

The distance AE represents the speed made good of nearly 6 knots.

Note: the speed arc _does not_ go through B, but can cut the line or extention of the line AB anywhere.

LATITUDE SCALE 1' OF LAT = 1 SEAMILE

SOURCES OF POSITION LINES

A PRUDENT NAVIGATOR USES AS MANY DIFFERENT POSITION LINES AS POSSIBLE TO GET A FIX. THIS IS ALSO A USEFUL WAY OF CHECKING ON THE ACCURACY OF ELECTRONIC NAVIGATION EQUIPMENT.

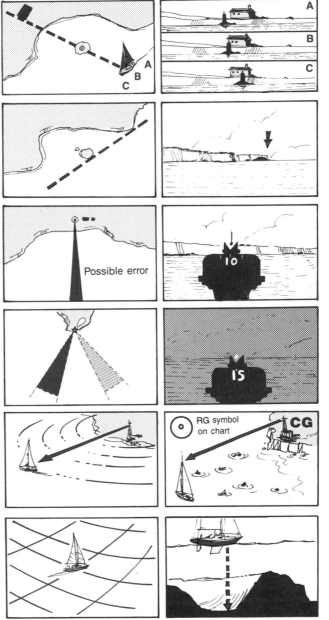

TRANSIT
When two charted objects line up (like this house and beacon) it gives a very accurate position line known as a transit. *(see page 34)*

Transits can be found all over charts by lining up, Church spires, water towers, Radio masts, ends of sea walls, buildings, beacons, buoys, and even edges of land. Care is needed here identifying the 'correct edge'.

A COMPASS BEARING can be taken on any charted object you can identify. Again, care is needed in allowing for the possible errors incurred. *(see page 12)*

SECTOR LIGHTS give a position line when they change colour or a compass bearing can be taken on any light. If they are just 'dipping' below the horizon a range can also be calculated *(see pages 17,31).*

R.D.F. (Radio, Direction, Finding) transmitters give a position line when the receiver is pointed at it and the signal disappears. *(see page 14)*Although, in an emergency the Coast Guard can give a position line from your ordinary V.H.F. transmissions.

ELECTRONIC AIDS like DECCA, LORAN and SATNAV give accurate fixes as well position lines *(see pages 15,16)* even a simple echo-sounder can be used to find an approximate position line by charting the shape of the sea bottom. *(see page 36)*

VARIATION is the angular difference between **TRUE NORTH** (top of world and top of chart) and **MAGNETIC NORTH** (what your compass should point at). As the magnetic field of the world is not constant, **MAGNETIC NORTH** gradually changes position.

This local **VARIATION** between **TRUE AND MAGNETIC NORTH** is shown on the compass rose printed on the chart.

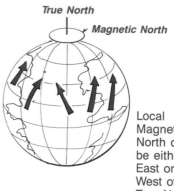

Local Magnetic North can be either East or West of True North

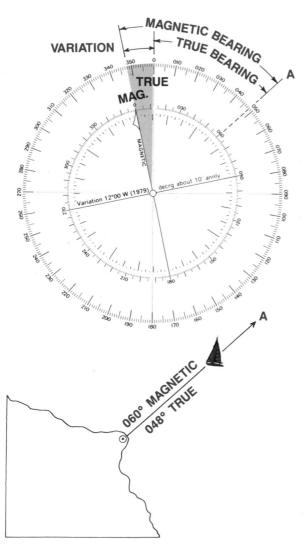

TRUE NORTH is pointing straight up while local variation was measured to be 12° WEST in 1979 *but decreasing* each year by 10' — so, in 1989 the **VARIATION** is only 10° 20' WEST.

Here we have a yacht off a well charted headland its **MAGNETIC BEARING** from the headland is 060° in 1979 and 58° 20' in 1989 but its **TRUE BEARING** is always 048°, no matter what year it is.

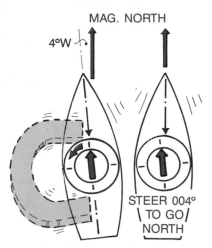

MAG. NORTH

4°W

STEER 004°
TO GO
NORTH

DEVIATION

Deviation is how far the magnetic influences of the boat pulls the compass needle away from Magnetic North. *Here it is pulled 4° West, so, to go North we need to steer 4° E.*

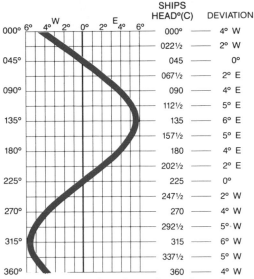

SHIPS HEAD°(C)	DEVIATION
000°	4° W
022½	2° W
045	0°
067½	2° E
090	4° E
112½	5° E
135	6° E
157½	5° E
180	4° E
202½	2° E
225	0°
247½	2° W
270	4° W
292½	5° W
315	6° W
337½	5° W
360	4° W

If the compass does have deviation, then it needs to be checked on each heading and a DEVIATION CURVE like this drawn up.

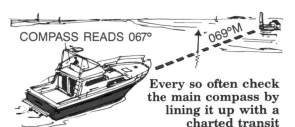

COMPASS READS 067°

069°M

Every so often check the main compass by lining it up with a charted transit

COMPASS NEEDLE PULLED 2°E

To check the main ship's compass compare its reading with that of an accurate hand bearing compass that is being towed behind in a dinghy well away from all magnetic influences.

These can range from beer cans to large lumps of metal like the keel.

ERROR WEST = COMPASS BEST
4° W means compass must read 4° more
ERROR EAST = COMPASS LEAST
4° E means compass must read 4° less

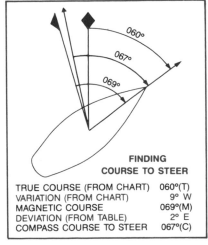

060°
067°
069°

**FINDING
COURSE TO STEER**

TRUE COURSE (FROM CHART)	060°(T)
VARIATION (FROM CHART)	9° W
MAGNETIC COURSE	069°(M)
DEVIATION (FROM TABLE)	2° E
COMPASS COURSE TO STEER	067°(C)

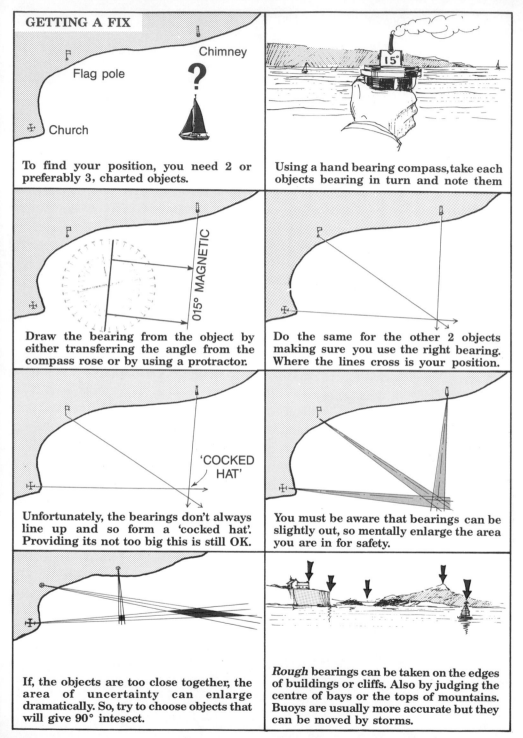

GETTING A FIX

Chimney

Flag pole

?

Church

To find your position, you need 2 or preferably 3, charted objects.

Using a hand bearing compass, take each objects bearing in turn and note them

015° MAGNETIC

Draw the bearing from the object by either transferring the angle from the compass rose or by using a protractor.

Do the same for the other 2 objects making sure you use the right bearing. Where the lines cross is your position.

'COCKED HAT'

Unfortunately, the bearings don't always line up and so form a 'cocked hat'. Providing its not too big this is still OK.

You must be aware that bearings can be slightly out, so mentally enlarge the area you are in for safety.

If, the objects are too close together, the area of uncertainty can enlarge dramatically. So, try to choose objects that will give 90° intesect.

Rough bearings can be taken on the edges of buildings or cliffs. Also by judging the centre of bays or the tops of mountains. Buoys are usually more accurate but they can be moved by storms.

TRANSFERRED POSITION LINES 'RUNNING FIX'

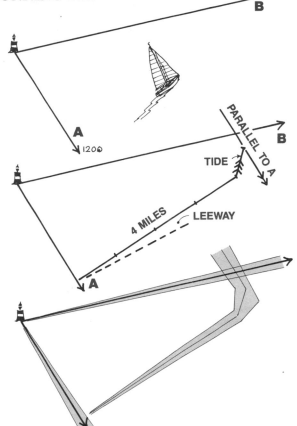

When only one identifiable object is visible these methods can be used.
At 1200 take bearing (A) and read the log.
At 1300 take bearing (B) and read the log.

Work out your position from any point on line (A), allowing for leeway and tidal set and drift.
Draw a line parallel to (A) from this position, until it cuts (B). Thats your approximate position at 1300.

It can only be approximate because:-

1. **The bearings might be out**
2. **The log might be out**
3. **The compass might be out**
4. **The tide might be out**

But an approximate position is better than nothing.

**RAIL MARKED AT 45°
FROM HELM POSITION**

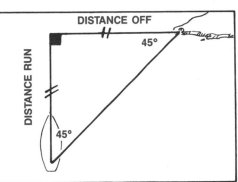

DISTANCE OFF

DISTANCE RUN

45°

45°

'A FOUR POINT AND ABEAM BEARING FIX'

If you read the log when an object bears 45° off the bow. (Some people mark their guard rail at 45° from their normal helming position to save using a compass).

When the object comes abeam the distance run (allowing for tide) is equal to the distance off. (Best around headlands where tide is either *with* or *against* you).

RADIO DIRECTION FINDING (RDF)

NO SIGNAL ON END OF AERIAL

RADIO CONTAINS INTERNAL ROD AERIAL

STRONG SIGNAL ON SIDE OF AERIAL

READ COMPASS WHEN SIGNAL STOPS

STRONG SIGNAL ON SIDE OF AERIAL

An R.D.F. beacon broadcasts a morse identification signal followed by a long tone. When you have identified the station, swing the radio until the internal aerial points, end-on to the transmitter and the signal disappears. Read the compass. A beat frequency oscillator (BFO) can be switched on to generate a sympathetic tone and makes the 'null' position easier to find.

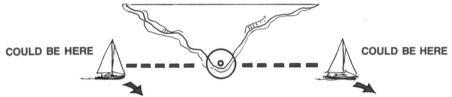

COULD BE HERE

COULD BE HERE

As the aerial has two ends, you could be pointing at, or away from the transmitter. So, if you are really lost steer safely out to sea and note how the bearing changes.

ERRORS RDF bearings are unreliable 1 hour each side of dawn and dusk.

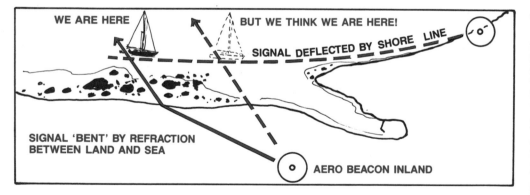

WE ARE HERE

BUT WE THINK WE ARE HERE!

SIGNAL DEFLECTED BY SHORE LINE

SIGNAL 'BENT' BY REFRACTION BETWEEN LAND AND SEA

AERO BEACON INLAND

Signals can be bent by travelling over land or along coastlines, so these cannot be relied on. Metal objects onboard can also affect radio signals and the compass in the set. Therefore, it is best to try and find a position in the boat where there is no inteference. This must also be away from long uninterrupted lengths of wire as these can also disturb incoming signals.

DECCA

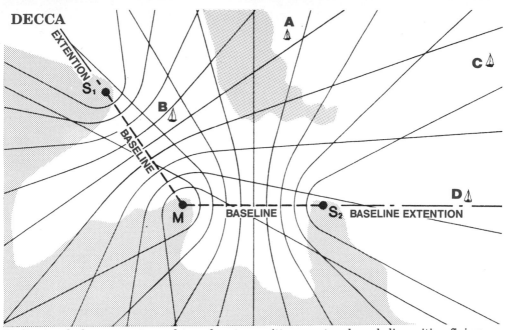

Radio signals from a *master* and two *slave* transmitters create a hyperbolic position fixing grid. The receiver onboard senses the phase difference between the master and slave signals and displays the position as either lat. and long. coordinates or DECCA grid reference numbers.

The accuracy can be affected by:-

- Grid pattern distorted by propigation differences between land and sea (Radio waves bend slightly when crossing between land and sea. This is a fixed error A).

- Range from the transmitters (max. 240 miles by day, less by night).

- Position in the grid — B will be more accurate than C due to the relative sizes of the grid 'diamonds'.

- Being too close to the *base line extension* (Position D). The cure is to switch to a different 'chain' of transmitters.

- Electrical interference onboard from powerful radios etc.

- Thunderstorms near the boat or worse still near the transmitter where you are unaware of them.

WAYPOINTS

A lat. or long. WAYPOINT position can be programmed into the set and the range of bearing to that point constantly read out. Some sets can also cope with tidal vectors, variation, deviation, speed and course over the ground as well as being interfaced with other electronic instruments.

REMEMBER — Decca is a navigation aid, not a navigation system. Keep both the plot on the chart and logbook up to date.

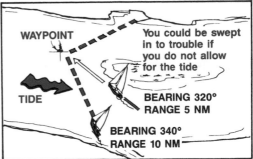

15

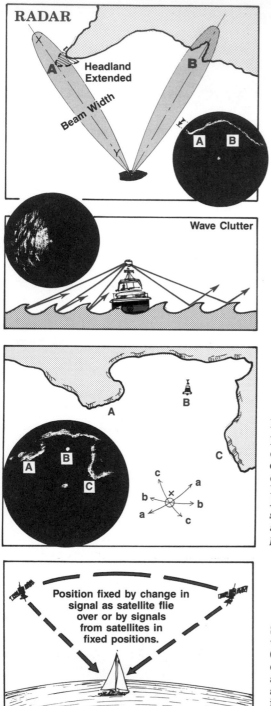

BEAM WIDTH

A radar beam sweeps through 360° and 'paints' a picture of the reflected signals. The beam width of a yacht's radar can be from 2° to 6° wide. So at *1 mile range* the beam could be about *200 metres across* and this gives problems:-

When the beam hits headland A, it starts to 'paint' but uses the aerials centre-line X-Y as its reference. This extends the headland picture and makes a bearing on it unreliable.

At B, the beam width is so wide it ignores the inlet and 'paints' a continuous coastline. But here the range is more reliable as the object is at 90° to the beam.

WAVE CLUTTER

Wave clutter is caused by the waves to windward reflecting the signals back better than those to leeward. This can be reduced by careful tuning, although heavy rain can still be a problem.

POSITION FIX BY RADAR RANGE.

Radar can be used to plot a position by using either a visual bearing and a radar range or three radar ranges. Here we have two conspicuous headlands A and B and buoy C. By striking off their ranges we get a fix at X. *BUT, as a line of parked cars can give a stronger signal than a low coastline, so care is always needed when interpreting a radar picture!*

SATELLITE NAVIGATION covers the whole world, while DECCA and LORAN (similar) only cover limited areas. Frequency of fixes varies from place to place in the world, and accuracy depends on user input of course and speed. A new generation system (G.P.S.) is currently planned to be fully operational in 1991.

DISTANCE OFF BY 'DIPPING' LIGHT

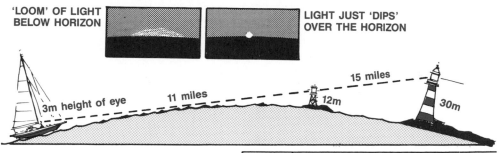

'LOOM' OF LIGHT BELOW HORIZON

LIGHT JUST 'DIPS' OVER THE HORIZON

15 miles

11 miles

3m height of eye

12m

30m

Due to the curvature of the earth a rough distance off a light of known height can be worked out when it just shows (or dips) over the horizon. Tables in almanacs make it easy:-

Here with an eye height of 3m we can see a 12m light at 11 miles and a 30m light at 15 miles.

Height of Light		HEIGHT OF EYE							
					Metres				
		1.5	③	4.6	6.1	7.6	9.1	10.7	1⁊
					Feet				
		5	10	15	20	25	30	35	ⵏ
m	ft								
⑫	40	9¾	⑪	11¾	12½	13	13½	14	1⵨
15	50	10¾	11¾	12½	13¼	14	14½	15	15
18	60	11½	12½	13½	14	14¾	15¼	15¾	16
21	70	12¼	13¼	14	14¾	15½	16	16½	17
24	80	13	14	14¾	15½	16	16½	17	1⁊
27	90	13½	14½	15½	16	16¾	17¼	17¾	18
㉚	100	14	⑮	16	16½	17¼	17¾	18¼	18

NAVIGATION BY SOUNDINGS

An accurate echo-sounder (see page 36) read at regular internals should give a picture of the sea-bed you are passing over. This is a useful distance check, if your course is to take you over a distinctive *trench* or *shoal* area. As well as warning you if you are heading towards the shallows.

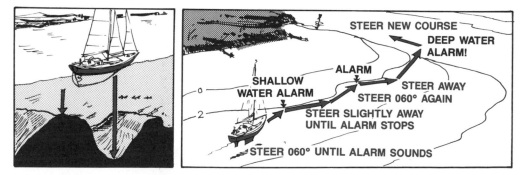

STEER NEW COURSE

DEEP WATER ALARM!

ALARM

SHALLOW WATER ALARM

STEER AWAY

STEER 060° AGAIN

STEER SLIGHTLY AWAY UNTIL ALARM STOPS

STEER 060° UNTIL ALARM SOUNDS

Deep and shallow water alarms are useful features on an echo sounder. By setting them (allowing for height of tide and depth of transducer) a quite accurate course can be made in restricted visibility, by following a depth contour line. Work out a course or courses to correspond to the contour line then zig-zag along it using the alarms.

TIDES

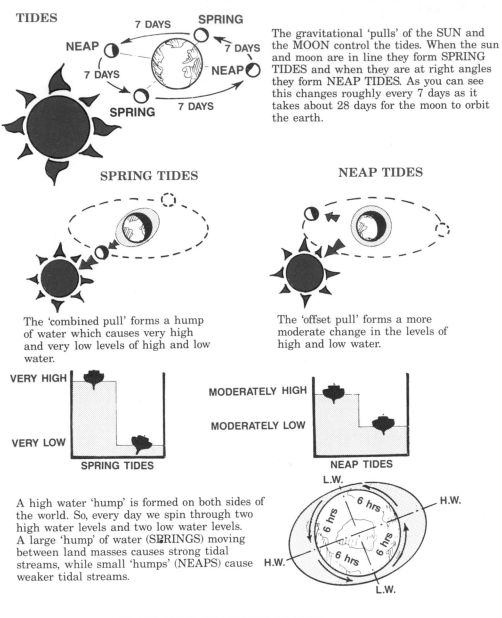

The gravitational 'pulls' of the SUN and the MOON control the tides. When the sun and moon are in line they form SPRING TIDES and when they are at right angles they form NEAP TIDES. As you can see this changes roughly every 7 days as it takes about 28 days for the moon to orbit the earth.

SPRING TIDES

The 'combined pull' forms a hump of water which causes very high and very low levels of high and low water.

NEAP TIDES

The 'offset pull' forms a more moderate change in the levels of high and low water.

A high water 'hump' is formed on both sides of the world. So, every day we spin through two high water levels and two low water levels. A large 'hump' of water (SPRINGS) moving between land masses causes strong tidal streams, while small 'humps' (NEAPS) cause weaker tidal streams.

VERY STRONG WINDS CAN 'HOLD' THE 'TIDE IN' OR PUSH THE 'TIDE OUT'

Unfortunately WIND and AIR PRESSURE can cause fluctuations in predicted levels.

TIDE TERMS

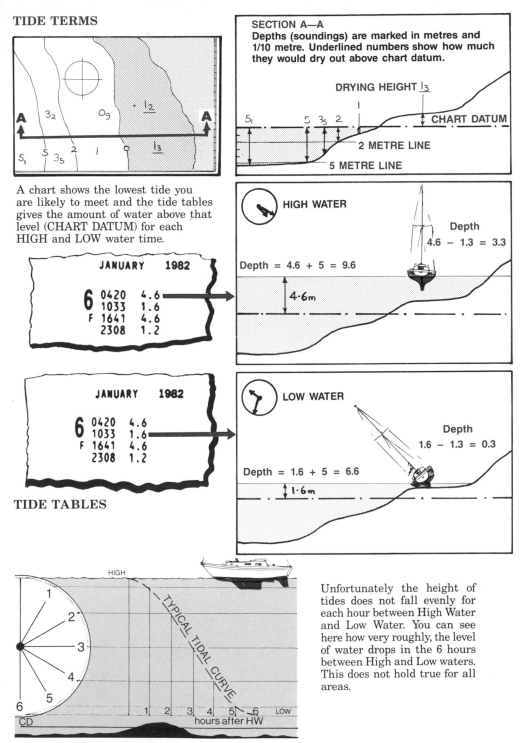

SECTION A—A
Depths (soundings) are marked in metres and 1/10 metre. Underlined numbers show how much they would dry out above chart datum.

DRYING HEIGHT $\underline{1_3}$

CHART DATUM

2 METRE LINE

5 METRE LINE

A chart shows the lowest tide you are likely to meet and the tide tables gives the amount of water above that level (CHART DATUM) for each HIGH and LOW water time.

JANUARY 1982

6 0420 4.6
1033 1.6
F 1641 4.6
2308 1.2

HIGH WATER

Depth = 4.6 + 5 = 9.6

4·6m

Depth
4.6 − 1.3 = 3.3

JANUARY 1982

6 0420 4.6
1033 1.6
F 1641 4.6
2308 1.2

TIDE TABLES

LOW WATER

Depth = 1.6 + 5 = 6.6

1·6m

Depth
1.6 − 1.3 = 0.3

HIGH

TYPICAL TIDAL CURVE

1 2 3 4 5 6 LOW
hours after HW

CD

Unfortunately the height of tides does not fall evenly for each hour between High Water and Low Water. You can see here how very roughly, the level of water drops in the 6 hours between High and Low waters. This does not hold true for all areas.

TIDAL TERMS

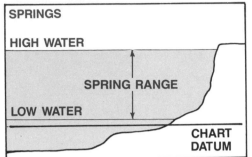

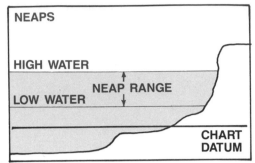

Mean High Water Springs M.H.W.S. is the average height of all the SPRING HIGH WATERS.

Mean Low Water Springs M.L.W.S. is the average height of all the SPRING LOW WATERS.

Mean High Water Neaps M.H.W.N. is the average height of all the NEAP HIGH WATERS.

Mean Low Water Neaps M.L.W.N. is the average height of all the NEAP LOW WATERS.

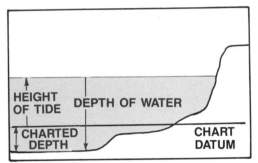

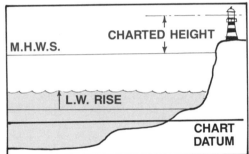

Height of tide is always measured from the CHART DATUM (lowest tide you are likely to meet) **Depths of Water** are measured from the HEIGHT to the sea bed. **Charted depth** is measured from CHART DATUM to sea bed.

Charted Heights, such as heights of lights or clearance under bridges, are always measured from M.H.W.S (The highest average tide height) **Rise of tide** is how much the water has risen from L.W. for that day.

MEASURING THE DEPTH

The depth of water can be measured with an echo-sounder. This measures the time differences between transmitted and reflected signals and converts them into depth readings. An allowance has to be made for the depth of the transducer in the hull and the keel.

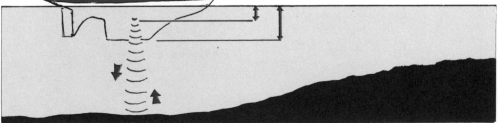

TIDAL CURVES provide a means of finding the height of tide between high and low water. *Example: At what time will there be 8 metres of water in St. Helier on 8th June?*

1. Refer to the tide table for 8th June.

2. Find the tidal curve for St. Helier (Nautical Almanacs).

3. Write in the H.W. time and fill in the boxes for each hour before H.W. (Rounding up or down) until you reach L.W. time.

4. Mark in the heights of H.W. and L.W.

5. Join the 9.2 to 3.2 with a line AB.

6. Find the 8 metre mark and drop a line until it hits AB.

7. Go horizontally until you reach the relevant curve for Springs or Neaps then drop down to find the time.

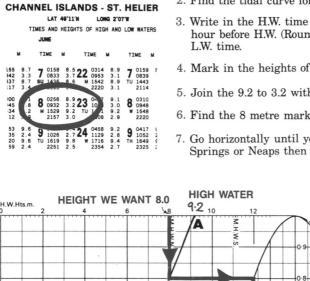

CHANNEL ISLANDS - ST. HELIER
LAT 49°11'N   LONG 2°07'W
TIMES AND HEIGHTS OF HIGH AND LOW WATERS
JUNE

M	TIME	M		TIME	M		TIME	M
155 8.7	7	0158 8.5	22	0314 8.9	7	0159 f		
142 3.3		0833 3.7		0953 3.1		0839		
137 8.7	SU	1436 8.6	M	1542 8.9	TU	1443		
17 3.4				2220 3.1		2114		
00	8	0256 8.9	23	04 9.1	8	0310		
45 .8		0932 3.2		10 3.0		0948		
34 .2	M	1529 9.2	TU	1 9.2	W	1548		
12		2157 3.0		08 2.9		2220		
53 9.6	9	1026 2.7	24	0458 9.2	9	0417		
35 2.4				1129 2.8		1052		
20 9.6	TU	1619 9.8	W	1716 9.4	TH	1649		
59 2.4		2251 2.5		2354 2.7		2325		

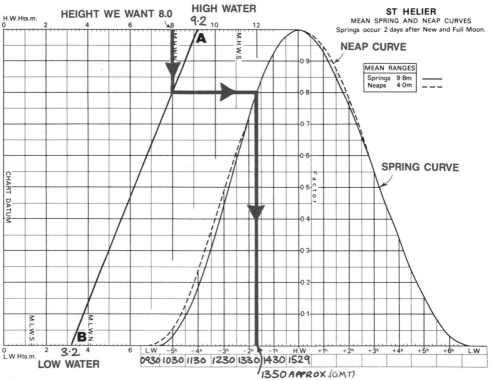

You can also find what height of tide there will be at a specific time by working backwards from the time scale ie. *How much water at 13.50?*. Go up to the curve, then horizontal to the line and up to the top scale = 8 metres.

SECONDARY PORTS

Nautical Almanacs publish the tidal height and time differences between large (STANDARD) ports and small (SECONDARY) ports.

ST HELIER .... TIME DIFFERENCES					HEIGHT DIFF.			
HIGH WATER		LOW WATER			MHWS	MHWN	MLWN	MLWS
0300 1500	0900 2100	0200 1400	0900 2100		11.1	8.1	4.1	1.3
BRAYE............ +0050	+0040	+0025	+0105		-4.8	-3.4	-1.5	-0.5

So, if H.W. is at 0300 or 1500 it will be 50 mins later at BRAYE
But, if H.W. is at 0900 or 2100 it will be 40 mins later at BRAYE
Also when there is 11.1 metres at H.W. at St. Helier then will be 4.8 metres less at BRAYE etc.

However, if high and low water falls between these set times, we must interpolate (estimate) between the "difference" figures. This can be done by eye but a graph is more accurate.

ST. HELIER time	height (m)
1647	3.2 L.W.
2233	9.2 H.W.

What time and height is low water at BRAYE?

Low Water BRAYE:- Time = 16.47 + 0040 = 17.27 GMT.
Height = 3.2 - 1.2 = 2 metres.

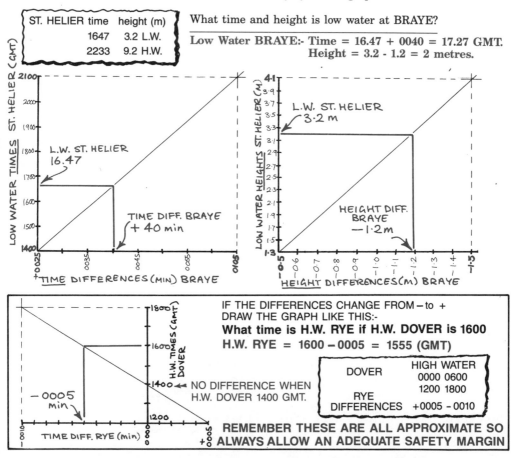

IF THE DIFFERENCES CHANGE FROM – to +
DRAW THE GRAPH LIKE THIS:-
What time is H.W. RYE if H.W. DOVER is 1600
H.W. RYE = 1600 – 0005 = 1555 (GMT)

NO DIFFERENCE WHEN H.W. DOVER 1400 GMT.

DOVER	HIGH WATER 0000 0600 1200 1800
RYE DIFFERENCES	+0005 – 0010

REMEMBER THESE ARE ALL APPROXIMATE SO ALWAYS ALLOW AN ADEQUATE SAFETY MARGIN

TIDAL ANOMOLIES

Unfortunately, some areas like those on the southcoast, do not conform to a neat symetrical graph but display a rather distorted shape as shown here. In these areas low waters are often easier to define than high water so the graph is based on times of low water.

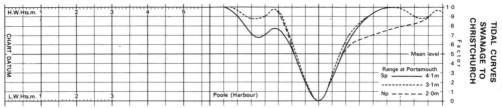

TIDAL STREAMS

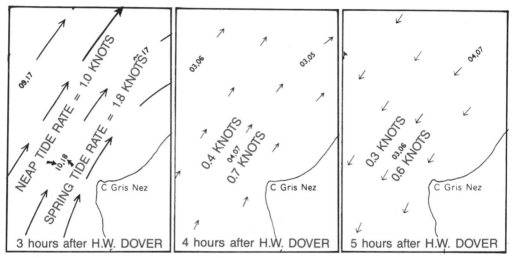

The *rate* and *direction* of tidal streams can be depicted in different ways:-

THE TIDAL STREAM ATLAS (above), by using a separate page for each hour either side of high water at a *standard port,* gives a more graphic display. So you can see at a glance when the tide turns but you must use a protractor to measure its direction.

THE TIDAL DIAMONDS (below) on the chart do the same job but the direction is given as a *TRUE BEARING.* The strength or *RATE* for the hour in both cases, has to be estimated if you are between *SPRING* AND *NEAP* tides

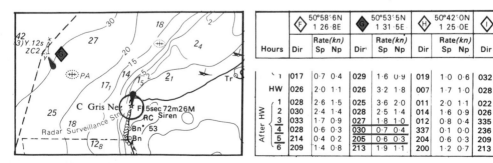

	◇ F 50°58·6N 1 26·8E			◉ G 50°53·5N 1 31·5E			◇ H 50°42·0N 1 25·0E			◇ 5(
Hours	Dir	Rate(kn) Sp	Np	Dir	Rate(kn) Sp	Np	Dir	Rate(kn) Sp	Np	Dir
`1	017	0·7	0·4	029	1·6	0·9	019	1·0	0·6	032
HW	026	2·0	1·1	026	3·2	1·8	007	1·7	1·0	028
After HW 1	028	2·6	1·5	025	3·6	2·0	011	2·0	1·1	022
2	030	2·4	1·4	028	2·5	1·4	014	1·6	0·9	026
3	033	1·7	0·9	027	1·8	1·0	012	0·8	0·4	335
4	028	0·6	0·3	030	0·7	0·4	337	0·1	0·0	236
5	214	0·4	0·2	205	0·6	0·3	204	0·6	0·3	209
6	209	1·4	0·8	213	1·9	1·1	200	1·2	0·7	213

23

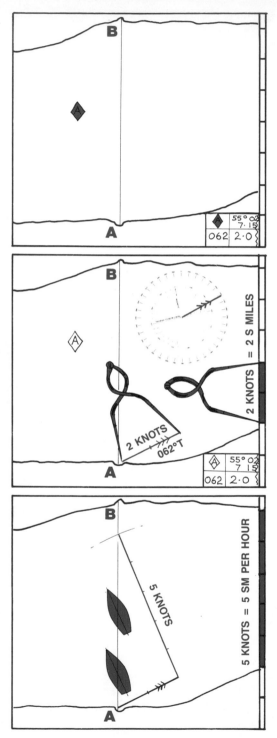

To go from A to B we find the nearest *tidal diamond* and check the *rate and direction* for the time we are travelling. That means the time in relation to the time of high water at the Standard Port.

We transfer the *true bearing of 062°* from the compass rose to our starting point and as we have a SPRING TIDE we can use the figure of 2 KNOTS. We measure 2 miles from the scale at the edge of the chart opposite our position.

ANY LINE DRAWN TO SCALE SHOWING A BEARING AND A SPEED IS KNOWN AS A 'VECTOR'.

From the end of the tidal vector we strike off an arc equal to the speed we hope to average on the trip, say 5 KNOTS. Where the arc cuts the line AB we draw a line which is our course. If we transfer this line back to the compass rose we get our course to steer. Again if there is any cross wind we must allow for leeway.

ALLOWING FOR SEVERAL TIDAL STREAMS

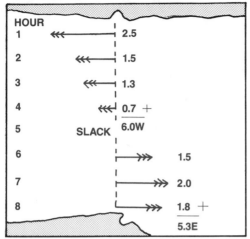

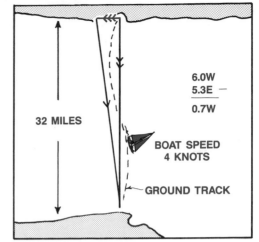

HOUR		
1	⪻⪻←	2.5
2	⪻←	1.5
3	⪻←	1.3
4	⪻←	0.7 +
	SLACK	6.0W
5		
6	→⪼⪼	1.5
7	→⪼⪼	2.0
8	→⪼⪼	1.8 +
		5.3E

32 MILES

6.0W
5.3E —
0.7W

BOAT SPEED
4 KNOTS

GROUND TRACK

When crossing a channel with opposing tidal streams:-

1. Measure the distance across (32 miles)

2. Guess boat speed (4 knts)

3. Work out time for crossing (8 hrs)

4. Add up all East and West going tidal streams for those hours.

5. Plot balance (0.7W)

6. Strike off distance travelled in time (4 knts x 8 hrs = 32 miles) to give course.

7. Apply leeway, variation and deviation.

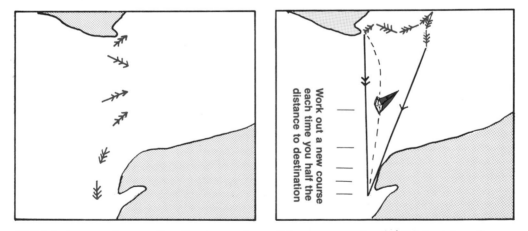

Work out a new course each time you half the distance to destination

If tidal streams change direction every hour it is necessary to plot tidal vectors for each hour.

From the end of the resultant tidal vector chain strike off the distance travelled (speed x time) to find the course.

But as everything can vary on a long passage, plot an E.P. every hour and work out a new course to steer each time you half the distance to your destination.

It is also good practice to 'aim off' so you arrive 'up-tide' of the harbour.

COURSE SHAPING

We are at A and want to know when to tack so we can clear the headland by ½ mile:-

Draw ½ mile radius around headland and mark in a water track at 045° to the wind. Measure down 5 miles for boat speed and draw in one mile at 180°T for tide. Mark in the ground track and extend it.

Work out the ground track from point A and extend it. Where the two ground tracks across (B) is the place to tack. The lengths of the ground track show we are only making 4.25 knots over the ground and the distance A-B is 7 miles. So we need to tack in about 1 hr 40 min.

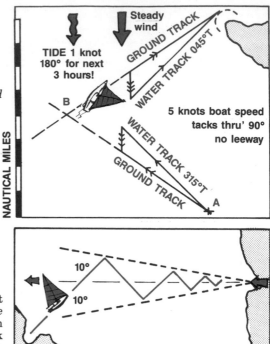

TACKING TO WINDWARD

If our destination is directly to windward, it is best to stay within 10° of the *down-wind line* to take advantage of any wind shifts which might occur. Always try to set off on the tack which is more directly towards the destination. But, if we have to allow for a change in tidal stream, an advantage is to be gained by letting the tide push us up to windward (as boat A is doing below).

The *tide* and *true wind* combine to form a

resultant wind or *tide induced wind* which is "lifting" boat A, and putting him in a good position when the tide turns. But the same *resultant wind* will be 'heading' boat B on his chosen tack and placing him in a poor position when the tide turns.

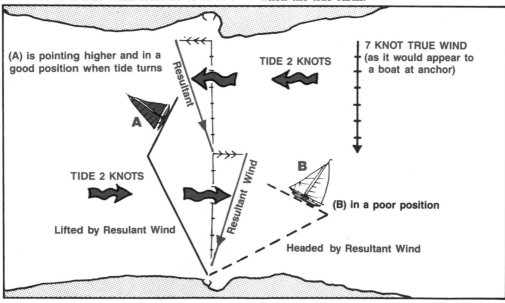

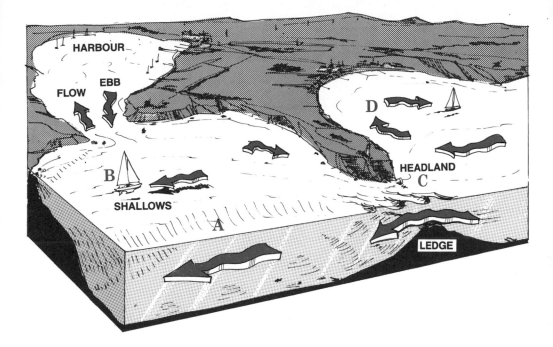

TIDAL EFFECTS

The shape of the seabed and surrounding land can greatly affect the speed and direction of tidal streams and local wave conditions:-

(A) In deep water offshore there is a strong tidal stream.

(B) Inshore in the shallower water the stream is less.

(C) Headlands and 'ledges' can increase the rate of flow and cause 'overfalls' as the water rushes and tumbles through the narrowed gap.

(D) Headlands and bays can also cause 'back eddies' where the tidal stream can actually turn back on itself and swirl in the opposite direction.

Both the reduced rate of flow in the shallows and the 'back eddies' along the the coast can be used to great advantage to sneak up over the tide. Local knowledge, pilot books, or a close-look at the tidal stream atlases will show where these areas are. At the same time the confused seas caused at headlands should be avoided by small craft by either going inshore or going further out to deeper water. Again, pilot books will advise on the best route to take.

BUOYAGE

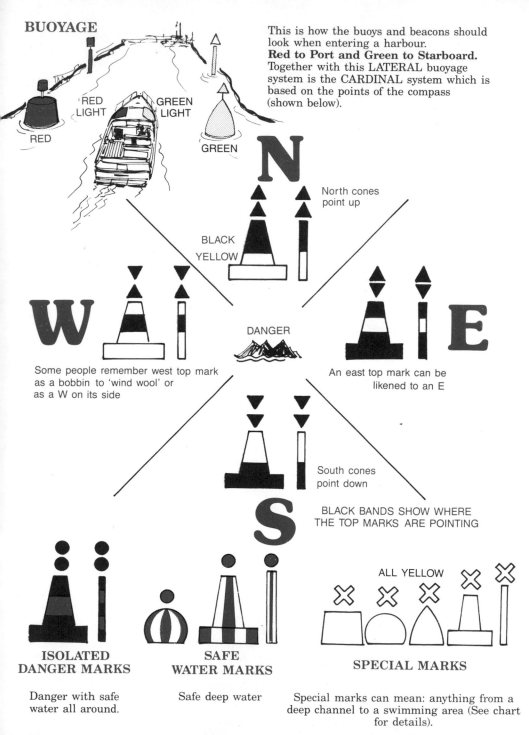

This is how the buoys and beacons should look when entering a harbour.
Red to Port and Green to Starboard.
Together with this LATERAL buoyage system is the CARDINAL system which is based on the points of the compass (shown below).

RED LIGHT

GREEN LIGHT

RED

GREEN

N

North cones point up

BLACK

YELLOW

W

Some people remember west top mark as a bobbin to 'wind wool' or as a W on its side

DANGER

E

An east top mark can be likened to an E

South cones point down

S

BLACK BANDS SHOW WHERE THE TOP MARKS ARE POINTING

ISOLATED DANGER MARKS

Danger with safe water all around.

SAFE WATER MARKS

Safe deep water

ALL YELLOW

SPECIAL MARKS

Special marks can mean: anything from a deep channel to a swimming area (See chart for details).

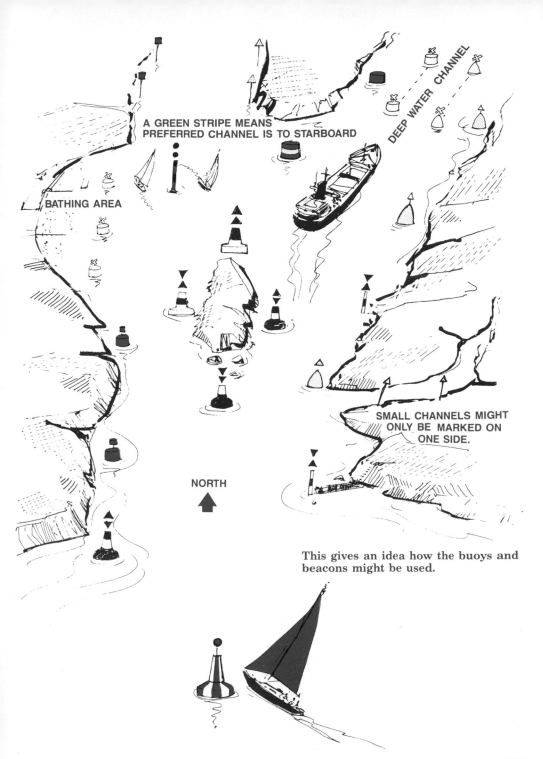

A GREEN STRIPE MEANS PREFERRED CHANNEL IS TO STARBOARD

DEEP WATER CHANNEL

BATHING AREA

SMALL CHANNELS MIGHT ONLY BE MARKED ON ONE SIDE.

NORTH

This gives an idea how the buoys and beacons might be used.

BUOYAGE

Buoys vary in size and construction. They often sport strange shaped radar reflectors, light platforms and solar or wind generators. Many have no top marks at all just a plain red or green buoy and in small channels there may only be a painted stick! Port and Starboard buoys have red or green lights but cardinal marks flash white, as below like the numbers on a clock.

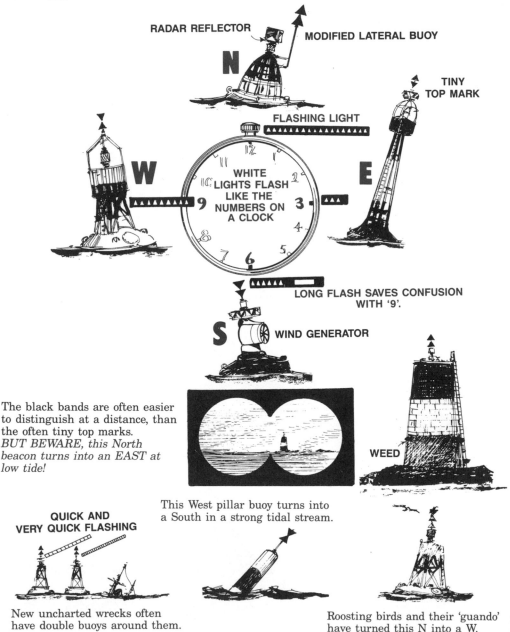

RADAR REFLECTOR

MODIFIED LATERAL BUOY

N

TINY TOP MARK

FLASHING LIGHT

W

WHITE LIGHTS FLASH LIKE THE NUMBERS ON A CLOCK

E

9

3

LONG FLASH SAVES CONFUSION WITH '9'.

S

WIND GENERATOR

WEED

The black bands are often easier to distinguish at a distance, than the often tiny top marks. *BUT BEWARE, this North beacon turns into an EAST at low tide!*

This West pillar buoy turns into a South in a strong tidal stream.

QUICK AND VERY QUICK FLASHING

New uncharted wrecks often have double buoys around them.

Roosting birds and their 'guando' have turned this N into a W.

30

LIGHTS

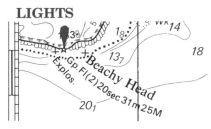

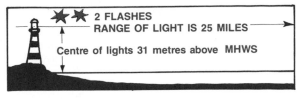

The abbreviations for lights are explained fully in (Admiralty booklet 5011), but this is what BEACHY HEAD is like.

Gp.F1 (2) 20 sec = 2 flashes every 20 secs.
31m = 31 metres above MHWS
25m = 25 mile range in good weather
Explos. = Explosive fog signal

SECTOR LIGHTS
Some lights have coloured sectors to indicated special navigational problems. Sometimes to show where the channel is — so if you stray to port you see red and if you stray to starboard you see green. Or, they can be used to cover a dangerous area but the chart or pilot book will give details.

LEADING LIGHTS
Harbour entrances are sometimes marked with 'leading lights'. When the lights line up you are in the channel. When they do not you can see which way to steer. The lower light is always in front.

LIGHT CHARACTERISTICS

Occulting (Oc) single more light than dark

Group occulting Oc (2)

Isophase (equal light & dark) Iso.

Single flashing F1.

Group flashing F1 (3)

Composite group flashing F1 (2 + 1)

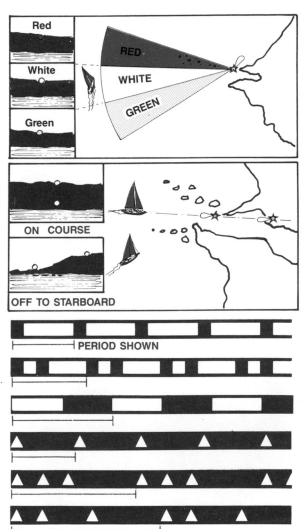

PILOTAGE

Pilotage is the skill of navigating in confined waters. There will seldom be time to plot fixes and EP's so you need to use other means to keep track of your position and course to steer.

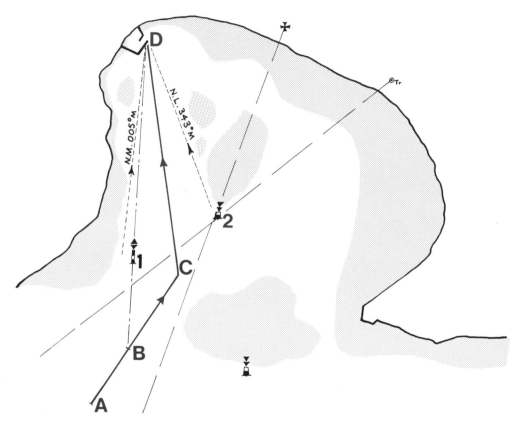

Pre-planning is essential:-

FROM A —   *Bn2 bears 018°(M). This gives a leading line through the shoals.*

AT B —   *The breakwater is in transit with Bn1 and should bear 001°(M). This will give a positive identification of the breakwater end.*

BETWEEN A & C — *Clearing transits are available in case you have to leave the plotted track.*

AT C —   *Alter course when breakwater end bears 355°(M) to steer towards it.*

BETWEEN C & D — *Clearing bearings on breakwater end. (No Less (N.L.) than 343°, No More (N.M.) than 005°.)*

SOUNDINGS —   *Watch the echo sounder it will warn you if you are going the wrong way.*

Beware of seeing "what you want to see"! The charted WHITE BUILDINGS, you have been looking for are there dead on course

BUT through the binoculars, turn out to be a brand new caravan site! This is a very easy mistake to make especially when you are tired.

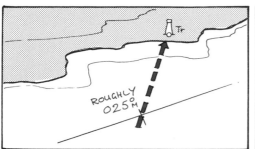

As it is not always easy to identify the landmark you are looking for check by measuring a rough bearing from your charted position.

Then go on deck and swing your handbearing compass onto that bearing. By looking near the bearing you should see the landmark you want.

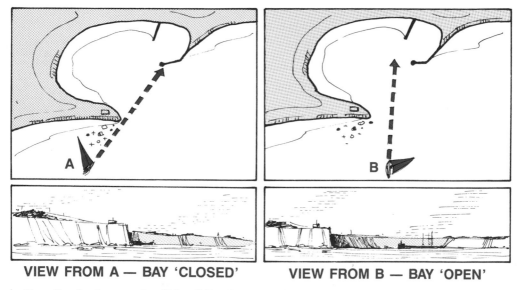

VIEW FROM A — BAY 'CLOSED'

From the chart we see that if the cliff and the end of the harbour wall line up we will be too close to the rocks.

VIEW FROM B — BAY 'OPEN'

So, provided the cliffs and the end of the harbour wall remain separated, or 'open' we will be in safe water.

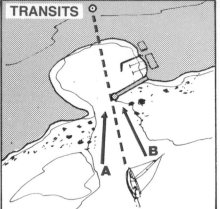

TRANSITS

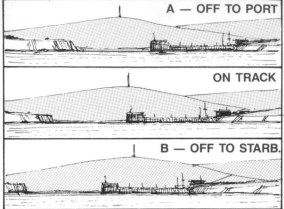

A — OFF TO PORT

ON TRACK

B — OFF TO STARB.

We are on course for the harbour when the end of the seawall and the beacon are in line. This is known as a transit.

So, when we are off track to port we shall see view (A) and if we are off track to starboard we shall see view (B).

TRANSIT PLUS BEARING

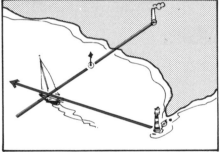

Transits can be found by lining up anything on the chart, like the edge of a building or breakwater, here we have a beacon and chimney.

The transit coupled with a bearing gives us a very good fix. The bearing of the lighthouse is taken when the the beacon and chimney are in line and it is transferred to the chart.

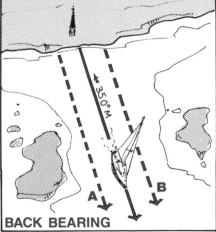

BACK BEARING

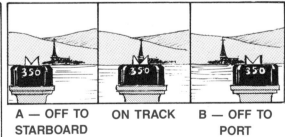

A — OFF TO STARBOARD   **ON TRACK**   **B — OFF TO PORT**

If the only available landmark is astern we shall need to take a back bearing, to see if we are off track. This can sometimes be awkward to work out so often it is easier to see what the correct bearing should be from the chart. Then set the hand bearing compass to it and see if we are to port of starboard of the desired line.

CLEARING LINES

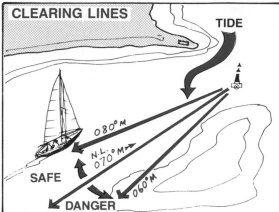

Here we have drawn a line at 070° mangetic to the North cardinal buoy. Provided our hand bearing compass always reads *more* than 070° we shall be clear of the shallow water. *N.L. (not less) 070°M.*

IN SAFE WATER

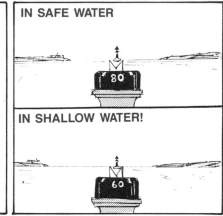

IN SHALLOW WATER!

This is what we might see:-
080° Magnetic is fine but if we get swept in by the tide until it read 060°M we are in trouble!

TWO CLEARING LINES

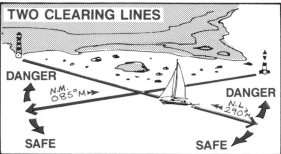

We can use two clearing bearings to sail around a potential hazard on our course. Over the stern 085° or *more* means trouble. While over the bow 290° or *less* is dangerous.

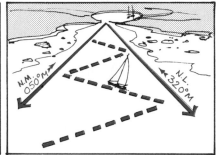

These bearings can be used to define the maximum area we can tack in. Any *lower* than 320° and any higher than 050° means trouble.

TURNING POINTS

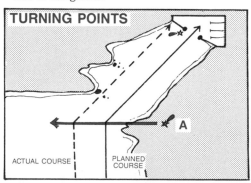

Here we have chosen to turn on to a new course when light (A) is abeam. But if we have been set slightly out say on to the dotted line we shall end up on the rocks.

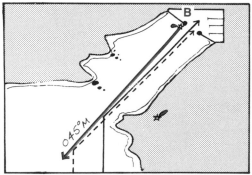

Much better to choose a turning point to align more closely to our new course. Say when light (B) bears 045°M then any error will be smaller and less dramatic!

ECHO SOUNDERS

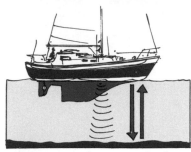

Echo sounders work by measuring the time differences between transmitted and reflected signals and converting them into a depth reading.

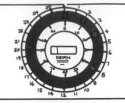

ROTATING NEON
Needs adjustment for clear reading. Can show type of bottom.

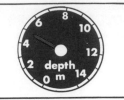

DIAL
Shows clearly depth *'falling'* or *'rising'* with analogue display.

DIGITAL
'Falling' and *'Rising'* sense sometimes added with arrows.

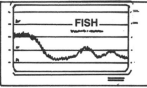

TRACE
Draws a *picture* of the bottom. Even fish shoals show up.

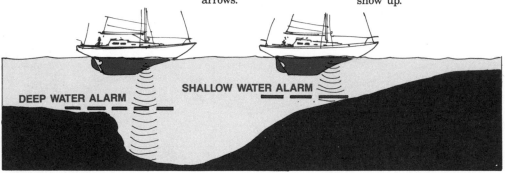

DEEP WATER ALARM

SHALLOW WATER ALARM

Alarms, which can be set to predetermined depths, are a useful feature. A *deep water alarm* will sound when passing over a *'trench'* as a position fixing guide. *Shallow water alarm* will sound when we are getting *too close to the edge!*

Checking
An allowance for the depth of the transducer in the hull has to be made when calculating depths. but the instrument itself needs checking occasionally with a 'lead line' (any weight on a graduated line).

A lead line also gives a much better 'picture' of the sea bottom when anchoring in an unfamiliar location.

LOGS

Speed used to be measured by the number of 'knots' pulled out by a *'LOG SHIP'* drogue in a set time.

KNOTS

LOG SHIP

TOWED MECHANICAL

Advantages
Simple, needs no batteries, can be moved from boat to boat.

Disadvantages
Cannot be adjusted onboard, line must be 'streamed' and 'handed'. Big fish eat spinners or they snag on the bottom in a calm.

TOWED ELECTRICAL

Advantages
Very accurate and can be calibrated. Spinner can be kept clear of fouling.

Disadvantages
Has to be 'streamed' and 'handed'.

THROUGH HULL

Advantages
Do not have to be streamed and always ready for use.

Disadvantages
Can foul easily with weed and then give a false reading.

ELECTRONIC (DOPPLER OR SONIC)

Advantages
Very accurate and nothing to foul.

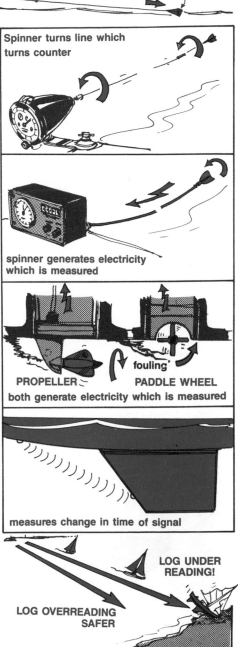

Spinner turns line which turns counter

spinner generates electricity which is measured

PROPELLER   PADDLE WHEEL
both generate electricity which is measured
fouling

measures change in time of signal

LOG UNDER READING!

LOG OVERREADING SAFER

All logs can go wrong and under or overread. So, they should be checked regularly against a known measured distance.

WEATHER SIMPLIFIED

HOT AIR RISES

COLD AIR FALLS TO TAKE ITS PLACE

When the sun heats the earth, the hot air rises and it is replaced by cold air. Just like a garden bonfire.

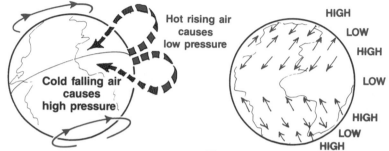

Hot rising air causes low pressure

Cold falling air causes high pressure

HIGH
LOW
HIGH
LOW
HIGH
LOW
HIGH

The spin of the earth disturbs this air movement and forms winds.

The uneven heating of the world cause bands of different pressure and winds.

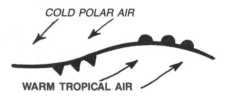

COLD POLAR AIR

WARM TROPICAL AIR

When warm and cold air systems meet they interact and form an eddy.

This swirls anticlockwise into a low pressure system called a *cyclone, depression* or *low.*

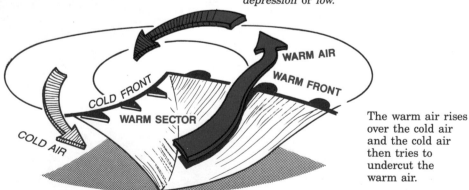

WARM AIR

WARM FRONT

COLD FRONT

WARM SECTOR

COLD AIR

The warm air rises over the cold air and the cold air then tries to undercut the warm air.

A weather map uses contour lines like an ordinary map but this time they represent areas of equal pressure. Hills are *'Highs'* hollows are *'Lows'*. The contour lines are known as isobars.

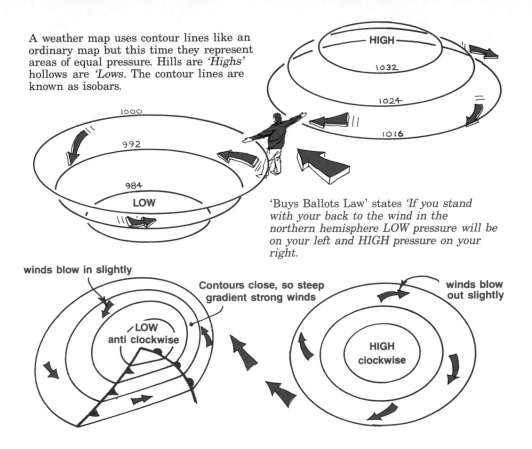

'Buys Ballots Law' states *'If you stand with your back to the wind in the northern hemisphere LOW pressure will be on your left and HIGH pressure on your right.*

Wind always blows from *HIGH* pressure to *LOW* pressure. (Like a leaking tyre) and the steeper the pressure gradient the stronger the wind.

DIRECTION OF MOVEMENT

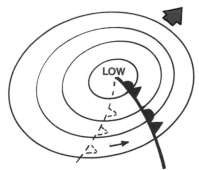

Lows can travel at speeds of 60 knots or more directed by the strong winds above them. But after several days it slows down and the cold front gradually catches up the warm one. When they joined it is known as an *'OCCLUDED FRONT'.*

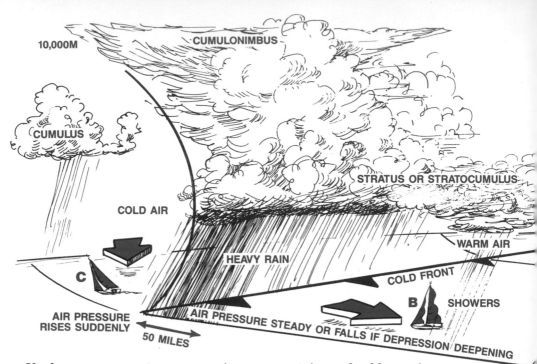

10,000M

CUMULONIMBUS

CUMULUS

STRATUS OR STRATOCUMULUS

COLD AIR

WARM AIR

HEAVY RAIN

COLD FRONT

C

B SHOWERS

AIR PRESSURE RISES SUDDENLY

AIR PRESSURE STEADY OR FALLS IF DEPRESSION DEEPENING

50 MILES

If a low pressure system was passing over us at A, we should experience:-

- *Wind increasing and backing as the warm front approaches.*
- *cloud building and thickening*
- *rain becoming heavier*
- *air pressure falling*
- *visibility deteriorating*

As the warm front passes:-

- *clouds nimbostratus*
- *rain turns to drizzle*
- *air pressure steady*
- *wind veers*
- *visibility poor*

In the warm sector at B

the wind and pressure is steady with occasional showers and poor visibility. As the cold front passes:-
- *wind very squally and veers*
- *cloud thickens*
- *heavy rain*
- *air pressure falls near front then suddenly rises*
- *visibility poor*

Behind the cold front at C:-

- *strong and gustly wind*
- *clear skies for a while*
- *air pressure steady*
- *visibility good*

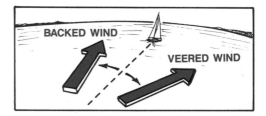

BACKED WIND

VEERED WIND

Centre of low approaching from between the directions of the high and low clouds.

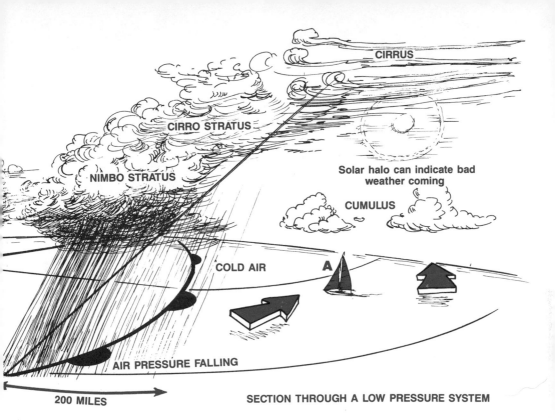

CIRRUS

CIRRO STRATUS

NIMBO STRATUS

Solar halo can indicate bad weather coming

CUMULUS

COLD AIR

A

AIR PRESSURE FALLING

200 MILES

SECTION THROUGH A LOW PRESSURE SYSTEM

WHAT WEATHER TO EXPECT

The main air masses affecting British waters are shown here on the right.
Their names explain what sort of general weather to expect from each direction;

ARTIC AND POLAR *COLD*

TROPICAL *WARM*

MARITIME *WET*

CONTINENTAL *DRY*

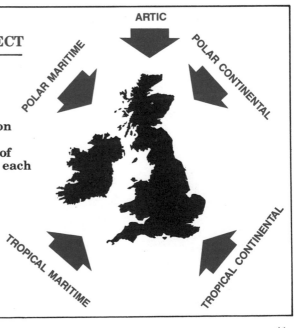

ARTIC

POLAR MARITIME

POLAR CONTINENTAL

TROPICAL MARITIME

TROPICAL CONTINENTAL

WINDS

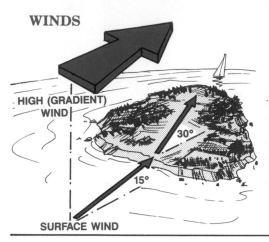

HIGH (GRADIENT) WIND

30°

15°

SURFACE WIND

Winds blowing at sea level are not only slowed by the friction of the earth's surface, but change direction as well.

Over water the wind is 'backed' by about 15° from the high wind direction. While over land the difference can be as much as 30°-40°.

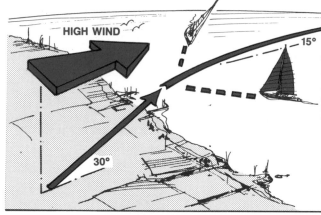

HIGH WIND

15°

30°

The difference between the direction of surface wind over land and water can be felt when tacking towards land.

When close in, port tack wind becomes 'freer' while the poor boat on starboard can be 'headed').

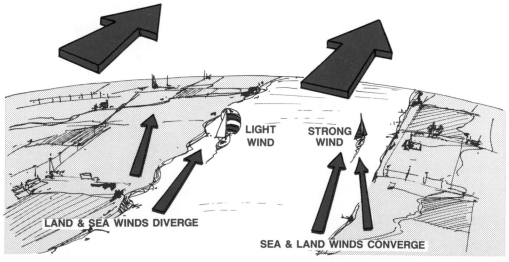

LIGHT WIND   **STRONG WIND**

LAND & SEA WINDS DIVERGE

SEA & LAND WINDS CONVERGE

Light coastal wind direction can be 'modified' by a 'sea breeze'.

Wind blowing off shore over cliffs can be very turbulent with strong eddies close in and bands of strong and light winds stretching far out to sea.

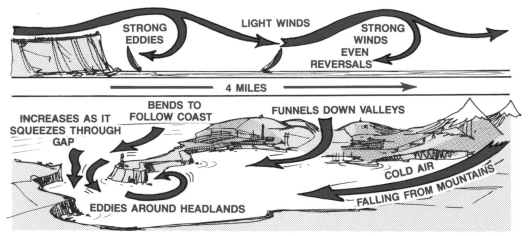

Both the speed and direction of the wind can be changed quite dramatically by the shape and temperature of the land.

FOG

Sea fog is formed as warm maritime air drifts northwards over colder water and picks up moisture on the way. When the air is cool enough the moisture condenses to form fog.

BEAUFORT SCALE OF WIND FORCE

Beaufort Number	General Description	Sea State	Velocity in in knots
0	Calm	Sea like mirror	less than 1
1	Light air	Ripples formed, no foam crests	1–3
2	Light breeze	Small wavelets, short but more pronounced. Crests glassy but do not break.	4–6
3	Gentle breeze	Large wavelets, crests start to break. Foam glassy, scattered white horses.	7–10
4	Moderate breeze	Small waves becoming longer, fairly frequent white horses.	11–16
5	Fresh breeze	Moderate waves, more pronounced long form, many white horses, some spray.	17–21
6	Strong Breeze	Large waves start to form, extensive white foam crests, spray.	22–27
7	Near Gale	Sea heaps up, white foam from breaking waves starts blowing in streaks along wind direction	28–33
8	Gale	Moderately high waves in greater length, Crests break off in spindrift, foam blown in well-marked streaks.	34–40

Note these are average speeds the yachtsman may experience one force higher in the gusts.

MEANINGS OF TERMS USED IN WEATHER FORECASTS

GALE WARNINGS: if the average wind is expected to increase to F8 or more, or gust of 43kn are expected. **SEVERE GALES** if the wind is expected to increase to F9 (41kn) or over, or gusts of 52 kn are expected.

STORMS: if the average wind is expected to increase to F10 (48kn) or over, or gusts of 61kn are expected.

IMMINENT: within 6 hours from time of issue of the warning.

SOON: between 6–12 hours from time to issue.

LATER: after 12 hours from time of issue.

WIND STRENGTHS: Land forecasts use the following: Calm = 0; Light = F1–3; Moderate = F4; Fresh = F5; Strong = F6–7; Gale = F8.

VISIBILITY: descriptions of visibility in shipping forecasts mean the following:
Good: more than 5nM
Moderate: 2–5nM
Poor: 1,100yds to 2nM
Fog: less than 1,100yds

Coastal station reports use the following:
Mist or haze: 1,100–2,200 yds
Fog: less than 1,100yds

FAIR: used when there is nothing significant. ie. no showers, mist, rain, etc.

PRESSURE and TENDENCY:
Steady: Change less than 0.1mb in 3 hrs
Rising or falling Slowly: Change 0.1 to 1.5mb in last 3 hrs.
Rising or Falling: Change 1.6 to 3.5 mb in last 3 hrs.
Rising or Falling Quickly: Change 3.6 to 6.0mb in last 3 hrs.
Rising or Falling Very Rapidly: Change of more than 6.0mb in last 3 hrs.
Now Falling, now rising: Change from rising to falling or *vice versa* within last 3 hours.

PRESSURE SYSTEMS, speed of movement:
Slowly: up to 15kn
Steadily: 15–25kn
Rather quickly: 25–35kn
Rapidly: 35–45kn.

GENERAL SYNOPSIS   at 1300 ~~GMT~~/BST 16th APRIL

L78 600W IRELAND NE sl 200 W BAIL at 1300
FT APP. VALENTIA st NE   T W SEA AREAS

Gales	SEA AREA FORECAST		Wind		Weather	Visibility
	Viking	⌐	V.3	S 4/5		9
	N. Utsire					
	S. Utsire					
	Forties	⌐				
	Cromarty	⌐	S3	5/6	occ •	m
	Forth					
	Tyne					
	Dogger	⌐				
	Fisher	⌐	N5	v 3/4		9
	German Bight					
	Humber	⌐	N4/5 → S3	4/5	occ •	9 → m
	Thames	⌐				
	Dover	⌐	W3	SW 4/5 (6)	occ •	m → p f pats l.
	Wight	⌐				
	Portland	⌐	SW4 → 5/6	(7)	occ •	m/p f pats.
	Plymouth	⌐				
	Biscay		SW4 → 5/6		• /9	m/p f pats
✓	Finisterre	⌐	SW 5-7 loc8		• → ∇	m/p → 9
✓	Sole					
	Lundy	⌐	SW 4/5 (6-7)		• → ∇	m loc p f pats at f.
	Fastnet					
	Irish Sea					
✓	Shannon		SW 5-7 loc8		• → ∇	m → 9
✓	Rockall		S 5-7 loc 8		• → ∇	m → 9
	Malin	⌐	S 4 → 5/6		occ •	m/9
	Hebrides					
✓	Bailey		SE 5-7 loc8		occ •	m/9
	Fair Isle	⌐	SE 4 → 5/6		occ •	m/9
	Faeroes					
✓	SE Iceland		SE 5-7 loc 8 E (4 in N at f.)			9

← Mark gale areas   ← Connect areas grouped in forecast.

COASTAL REPORTS (Shipping Bulletin) at 1600 BST/GMT	Direction	Force	Weather	Visibility	Pressure	Trend
Tiree	S'E	3		11	10	
Butt of Lewis	S'E	3		10	11	
Sumburgh	SE'S	4		9	15	
Bell Rock	SE'S	4		8	13	
Dowsing	SE	1		5	17	
Dover	SW	3		5	18	
Royal Sovereign	SW	4		11	18	
Channel L.V.	SW	4		3	19	
Scilly	SSW	4	,	4	16	
Valentia	S'W	4	•,	2	10	
Ronaldsway	SW'S	3	•	5	12	
Malin Head	SSE	3	•	8	10	
Jersey						

COASTAL REPORTS (Inshore Waters) at BST/GMT	Direction	Force	Weather	Visibility	Pressure	Trend
Boulmer						
Spurn Head						
Walton on the Naze						
St. Catherine's Point						
Land's End						
Mumbles						
Valley						
Blackpool						
Prestwick						
Benbecula						
Stornoway						
Lerwick						
Wick						
Aberdeen						
Leuchars						

45

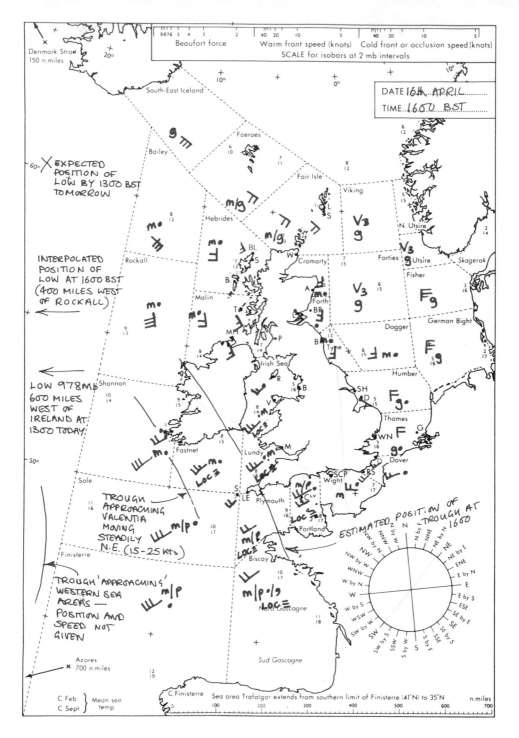

Beaufort force   Warm front speed (knots)   Cold front or occlusion speed (knots)
SCALE for isobars at 2 mb intervals

9876 5 4   3   2   40 20   10   5   40 20   10   5

Denmark Strait
150 n.miles

South-East Iceland

DATE 16th APRIL
TIME 1600 BST

Bailey

EXPECTED
POSITION OF
LOW BY 1300 BST
TOMORROW

Faeroes

Fair Isle

Viking

Hebrides

INTERPOLATED
POSITION OF
LOW AT 1600 BST
(400 MILES WEST
OF ROCKALL)

Rockall

Malin

Cromarty

Forties

Utsire

Skagerak

Fisher

Forth

German Bight

Dogger

Irish Sea

Tyne

Humber

LOW 978MB
600 MILES
WEST OF
IRELAND AT
1300 TODAY

Shannon

Fastnet

Lundy

Thames

Dover

Sole

TROUGH
APPROACHING
VALENTIA
MOVING
STEADILY
N.E. (15-25 Kts)

Plymouth

Wight

Portland

ESTIMATED POSITION OF TROUGH AT 1600

Finisterre

TROUGH 'APPROACHING'
WESTERN SEA
AREAS —
POSITION AND
SPEED NOT
GIVEN

Biscay

Nord Gascogne

Azores
700 n.miles

Sud Gascogne

C Feb.
C Sept. } Mean sea
temp.

C.Finisterre   Sea area Trafalgar extends from southern limit of Finisterre (41°N) to 35°N

100   200   300   400   500   600   700   n.miles

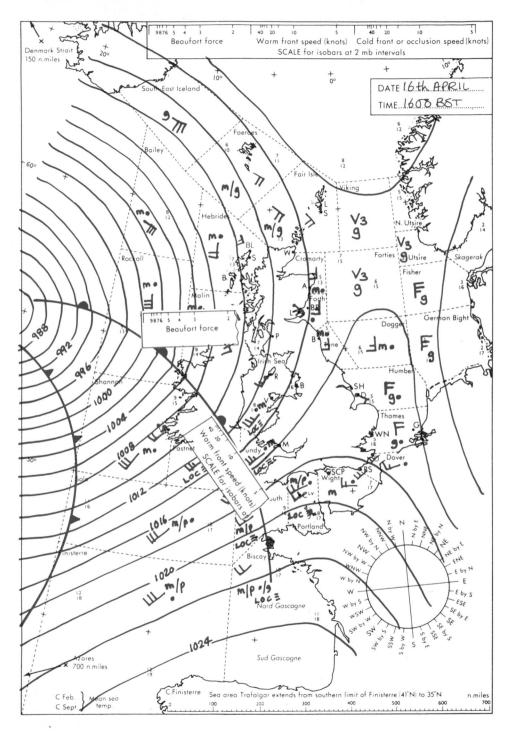

ANCHORING

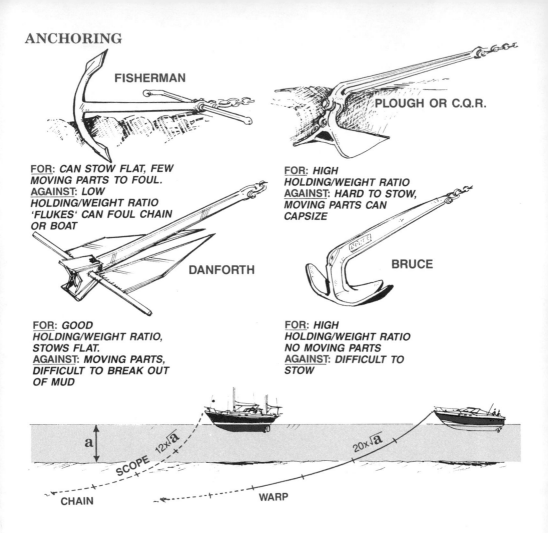

FISHERMAN

FOR: *CAN STOW FLAT, FEW MOVING PARTS TO FOUL.*
AGAINST: *LOW HOLDING/WEIGHT RATIO 'FLUKES' CAN FOUL CHAIN OR BOAT*

PLOUGH OR C.Q.R.

FOR: *HIGH HOLDING/WEIGHT RATIO*
AGAINST: *HARD TO STOW, MOVING PARTS CAN CAPSIZE*

DANFORTH

FOR: *GOOD HOLDING/WEIGHT RATIO, STOWS FLAT.*
AGAINST: *MOVING PARTS, DIFFICULT TO BREAK OUT OF MUD*

BRUCE

FOR: *HIGH HOLDING/WEIGHT RATIO NO MOVING PARTS*
AGAINST: *DIFFICULT TO STOW*

Whichever type of anchor you choose it will work best if the pull on it is close to horizontal. To achieve this the anchor line must be given plenty of 'SCOPE'.

If using chain the scope would be *12 x√max. depth of water expected.*

Nylon rope also absorbs shock but needs at least *20 x√the depth of water* to give a fair pull on the anchor. A length of chain (at least 5m) near the anchor guards against chafe and helps the anchor dig in.

In bad weather where the boat is pitching and snatching a scope of 10 times the depth of water may be needed. *"If in doubt, let more out!"* chain does more good on the sea bottom than in your chain locker!

Simple 'rule of thumb' approximations for scope are, for chain, 4 x depth for warp, 6 x depth.

TRIPPING LINES

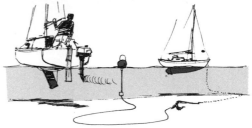

If you anchor in an area where you think the anchor might get stuck, add a tripping line to the other end. This lets you pull it clear if it jams.

Tripping lines can foul propellers or keels at low tide, so add a weight, or piece of chain, to sink it.

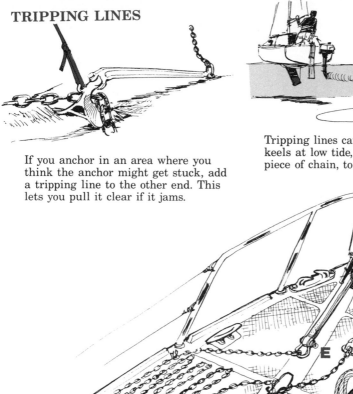

PREPARING TO ANCHOR
Good preparation can make all the difference:-

(**A**) Mark the chain to see how much to let out.

(**B**) Flaking the chain down prevents snarl-ups when you let go.

(**C**) Secure to the cleat so you can always let out more line.

(**D**) Rig a tripping line if you are worried about the anchor fouling on the bottom.

(**E**) *"Mouse"* shackle pin with wire to prevent it undoing as anchor moves on sea bed.

RULES OF THE ROAD

If an approaching vessel maintains the same bearing to you, there will be a collision. Check with a hand bearing compass. Or, if you are on a steady course, line him up with a stanchion, to see if he moves relative to you.

SAIL

OPPOSITE TACKS
Port gives way to starboard

SAME TACK
Boat to windward gives way

If in doubt a close-hauled port-tack gives way.

OVERTAKING
Any vessel POWER OR SAIL hass to give way when approaching another in this sector.

POWER

Head-on both turn to starboard

A

(A) has to give way to any vessel in this sector

WHO GIVES WAY TO WHO!

Power gives way to:-
● Sail
● Vessel fishing
● Vessel that can't manoeuvre

Sail gives way to:-
● Vessel fishing
● Vessel that can't manoeuvre

YOU MUST ALWAYS KEEP A GOOD LOOKOUT

SHIPS

What might seem a large expanse of water to us is *in fact a narrow channel* to a deep draught vessel. That is why small vessels must keep clear of large vessels in narrow channels.

Travelling at *over 30 knots* todays ships can come from below the horizon to your position *in less than 10 mins.*

SEPARATION LANES

In congested areas ships travel along lanes which are clearly marked on charts. Small boats should avoid crossing them, but if they must they should try to cross at a right angle.

(A) For sailing boats it's best to *steer at right angles* and be quickly swept across by the tide at a slight angle.

(B) To try to maintain a *course made good at right angles* could mean battling against the tide for hours and spending more time in the lanes than necessary. Try to avoid sailing across lanes in fog and when the winds are light.

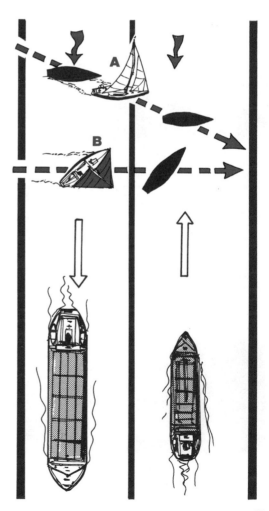

LIGHTS

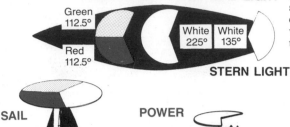

SIDELIGHTS **MASTHEAD LIGHT**

Green 112.5°

White 225° | White 135°

Red 112.5°

STERN LIGHT

These are the lights that a yacht should show at night. The colours and cut-off angles give others a clue to what you are and the direction you are travelling in.

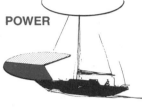

POWER

SAIL

Undersail a boat under 20 metres can show a combined RGW at the masthead.

POWER

Under power a white masthead light must show at least 1m above the RG sidelights.

A boat under 12m can show a white all round combined masthead and stern light when under power.

When sailing in rough seas a combined RGW masthead light is easier to sea than one mounted lower down.

Yachts are even harder to see at night. Bright navigation marks and other ships lights over power the tiny yachts light in the foreground.

Ships lights can be lost against a background of shore lights. So take extra care when near the coast or entering harbour.

Fishing boats *special* lights can be lost in the blaze of deck lights. So, it is best to keep well clear of large fleets at night.

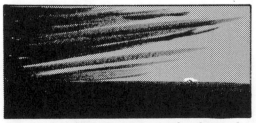

Beware of making the easy mistake of wrongly identifying a set of lights — this flood lit, slow moving, fishing boat way off on the horizon...

... could turn out to be an ocean liner ablaze with light travelling at over 30 knots which could be on top of you in a matter of minutes!

WHAT YOU SEE IN DAYLIGHT

WHAT YOU SEE AT NIGHT

AT ANCHOR

MOTORSAILING

The relationship between a ships 2 white masthead lights shows which direction it is travelling.

The front masthead white light is the lower

FISHING   FISHING GEAR OUT 150M IN THIS DIRECTION

TRAWLING

PILOT VESSEL   **HOVERCRAFT**

ALL ROUND FLASHING YELLOW LIGHT

TOWING   **VESSEL CANNOT MANOEUVRE**

over 200m

RESTRICTED IN ABILITY TO MANOEUVRE BUT MAKING WAY.

MINE SWEEPING   **UNDER WATER WORK**

SAFE SIDE   DANGER SIDE

VESSEL CONSTRAINED BY HER DRAUGHT

(should show a cylinder but rarely seen)

SAFETY EQUIPMENT NEEDED

Bailing and Bilge Pumping
(A) Hand Bailers (B) Buckets with strong handles and lanyard (C) Bilge pumps.

Detection Equipment
(D) Radar reflector (E) Navigation lights (F) Foghorn (G) Powerful waterproof torch.

Fire Fighting Equipment
(H) Fire blanket (I) 2 Fire extinguishers (1.5 kg) Dry powder or (J) (1.5 kg) BCF (K) Automatic extinguisher for engine

Personal Safety Equipment
(L) Life jacket (M) Buoyancy aid (N) Safety harnesses (O) Liferaft

Man Overboard Equipment
(P) A dan buoy is easier to see than a person (Q) Life belt with (R) drogue and (S) self-igniting light (T) Boarding ladder

General Equipment
(U) Tender (V) Various warps for towing and mooring (W) Tools and spare parts (X) Emergency water supply (Y) Large fenders

A large first aid kit should also be carried and like all safety equipment *you should know how to use it.* Try to attend a course to practise using all the different types of safety gear you carry.

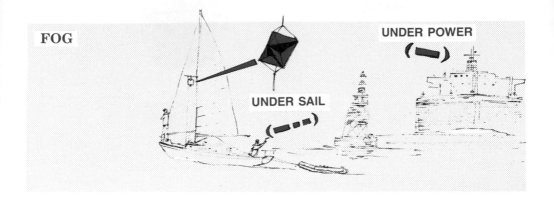

FOG

UNDER POWER

UNDER SAIL

HEAVY WEATHER

A force 5 can be 'heavy weather' to a small family cruiser with an inexperienced crew, while a larger boat with a strong crew can cope with a force 8 or more.

Listen to the weather forecast before you go
As skipper, if you have any doubts about your boat, your crew or yourself in the forecast conditions *don't go!*
It is a hard decision to make but better a disaapointed crew than one which is frightened off cruising for ever.

HEAVY WEATHER CHECK LIST

BELOW

- *All gear securely stowed (not depending on gravity)*

- *Easy to cook or pre-prepared food in accessible lockers*

- *Storm sails ready*

- *Navigation pre-planned as much as possible — with diversion plans*

ON DECK

- *All gear secured*

- *Reefing - lines rigged*

- *Jackstays rigged (if not permanent)*

PEOPLE

- *Warm and waterproof*

- *Get as much rest as possible*

VHF RADIO DISTRESS CALL

A distress call is sent when there is *GRAVE AND IMMINENT* danger to a vessel or person and *IMMEDIATE ASSISTANCE* is required.

HOW TO SEND A DISTRESS CALL.

Switch on power, Switch on radio, *select CH16* Turn to high power Push press-to-transmit switch and speak slowly and distinctly.

- MAYDAY, MAYDAY, MAYDAY.

Turning on the set etc. can be forgotten in an emergency so make up a reminder card and stick it up near the radio.

MAYDAY is the international distress signal.

- This is (Yacht's Name 3 times)

- MAYDAY (Yacht's Name)

The 'name' and the word 'yacht' helps the searchers know what they are looking for. See below

- Position (see below)

- Nature of Distress

- Any extra information which might help

"I require immediate assistance" and include number of people on board, whether you are going to abandon ship or have fired flares etc.

- Over

'Over' means please reply.

AN URGENCY CALL

An urgency call is used when you have a *very important* message to send covering *safety*.

PAN PAN, PAN PAN, PAN PAN,
Hello all stations (3 times) this is (Yacht's name 3 times)
- Position
- Nature of Urgency
- Assistance Required
- Over

The advantage of an urgency call is that it lets the world know you are in some sort of trouble without launching all the rescue services at that moment.

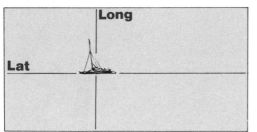
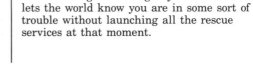

POSITIONS *MUST BE GIVEN IN LAT. LONG OR TRUE BEARINGS AND DISTANCE FROM A WELL DEFINED CHARTED POSITION*

If it is onboard, an Emergency Position Indicating Radio Beacon (or EPIRB) should be activated to raise the alarm and help the rescue services home in on you.

DISTRESS SIGNALS

Marine pyrotechnics are a simple way of sending a distress signal. make sure *all* the crew know how to fire them. This is the *minimum* you should carry.

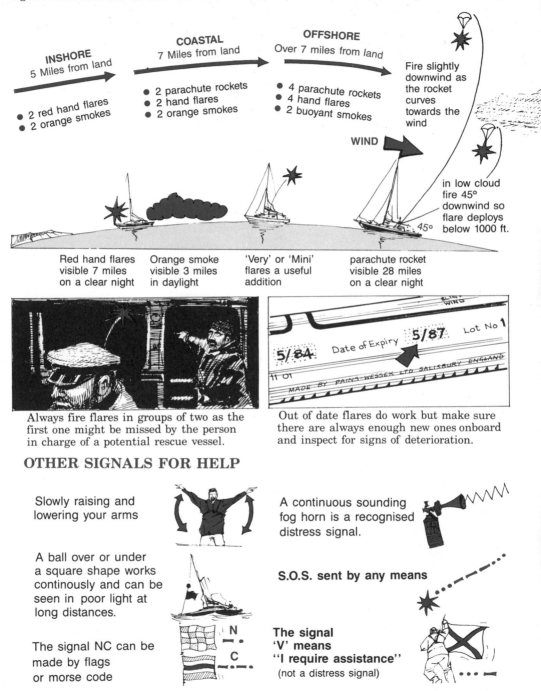

INSHORE
5 Miles from land

- 2 red hand flares
- 2 orange smokes

COASTAL
7 Miles from land

- 2 parachute rockets
- 2 hand flares
- 2 orange smokes

OFFSHORE
Over 7 miles from land

- 4 parachute rockets
- 4 hand flares
- 2 buoyant smokes

Fire slightly downwind as the rocket curves towards the wind

WIND

in low cloud fire 45° downwind so flare deploys below 1000 ft.

45°

Red hand flares visible 7 miles on a clear night

Orange smoke visible 3 miles in daylight

'Very' or 'Mini' flares a useful addition

parachute rocket visible 28 miles on a clear night

Date of Expiry   5/84   5/87   Lot No 1

MADE BY PAINS WESSEX LTD SALISBURY ENGLAND

Always fire flares in groups of two as the first one might be missed by the person in charge of a potential rescue vessel.

Out of date flares do work but make sure there are always enough new ones onboard and inspect for signs of deterioration.

OTHER SIGNALS FOR HELP

Slowly raising and lowering your arms

A ball over or under a square shape works continously and can be seen in poor light at long distances.

The signal NC can be made by flags or morse code

N
C

A continuous sounding fog horn is a recognised distress signal.

S.O.S. sent by any means

The signal 'V' means "I require assistance"
(not a distress signal)

57

LIFEBOAT While waiting for the lifeboat try to rig a bridle to spread the considerable towing loads over as many strong points as possible.

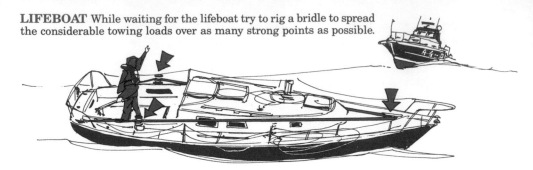

HELICOPTERS

DON'T — fire a flare near a helicopter (They'll lose night vision)
DON'T — touch the winch man in the air (you might get an electric shock!)
DON'T — attach the wire to the boat (unless asked to do so)
DO — launch the liferaft if asked (to keep all clear of mast)
DO — take to the water in life jackets if asked (for the same reason)

LIFERAFTS

UNLESS THE BOAT IS SINKING FAST, OR ON FIRE, DON'T USE THE LIFERAFT. You will stand more chance of being rescued, and suffer less from exposure in a flooded boat, than in a tiny liferaft.

Before launching all crew should put on warm clothes, oilskins and lifejackets. Also have ready *extra* emergency equipment eg. flares, EPIRB, water, food, space blankets.

The static line, once attached to the boat, might have to be pulled 25ft or more before inflation. Put a strong man in first for stability and to help weaker members aboard.

Cut the static line, stream the drogue to stop drift and add stability. Unplug the light during the day to save battery power.

Close main canopy, take seasick tablets, post a look-out, inflate double floor, tie in pump, spread out weight in rough weather or huddle together to keep warm.

THE RESCUERS ARE THE EXPERTS DO EXACTLY AS THEY SAY

FIRE
REMEMBER FIRE NEEDS:-
HEAT, FUEL AND *OXYGEN* CUT OUT ANY ONE AND THE FIRE GOES OUT.

CHECK BOAT FOR POTENTIAL FIRE HAZARDS — Such as:-
defective wiring, oil in bilge, accumulated waste paper or rags in lockers, suspect fuel or gas fittings.

NEVER smoke while refuelling or in a bunk.

ALWAYS turn the gas off at the bottle, 'earth' fuel filler pipes, fit flame traps on fuel tank vent pipes.

GAS HAZARDS Liquid petroleum gas is heavier than air so sinks into the bilges, if care is not taken. ALWAYS TURN OFF AT THE BOTTLE and let the gas burn out of the pipe. Then turn off at the stove. The bottle locker **MUST** drain overboard. A gas-detector is useful.

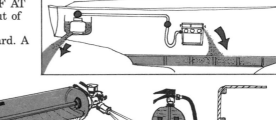

EXTINGUISHERS

DRY POWDER
(Colour coded blue)
Best stowed on side so powder keeps getting shaken up.

HALON OR BCF
(Colour coded green)
Don't use any extinguisher on its side (to get under a door etc) as only half the gas or powder will come out.

This type lets you get into awkward places.

A small FIRE FIGHTING HOLE (A) is better than opening the engine box. An AUTOMATIC GAS TYPE (B) is best for this area.

DRY POWDER is very messy but does smother fire and stops reignition. Gas can fill awkward spaces but is toxic if breathed for long periods.

Don't forget water splashed from a bucket works better than tipping it on to a fire.

FIRE BLANKETS
FIRE BLANKETS (or wet dish cloths) can put out a galley fire. They are also essential for clothing fires —
- push the person over so flames rise away from face.
- Don't roll over, it spreads the fire
- Smother flames away from face with fire blanket or any suitable cloth.

SINGLE LETTER CODES

'I' I AM TURNING TO PORT

(■■)

Although radio has taken over most communication between vessels, signals made by sound, flashing light and flags are still used. They are so comprehensive and agreed internationally, that a foreign doctor could give medical advise to a British Skipper without using a word of English!

'E' I AM TURNING TO STB

(■)

FIVE OR MORE BLASTS ON THE WHISTLE ARE USED TO WARN ANOTHER VESSEL OF YOUR PRESENCE.

(■■■)

'S' MY ENGINES ARE IN REVERSE (SLOWING DOWN OR ACTUALLY GOING ASTERN)

A full list of International code signals is published in an Admiralty Book

A . _   *I have a diver down; keep well clear at slow speed.*

D _ . .   *Keep clear of me — I am manoeuvring with difficulty.*

F . . _ .   *I am disabled. Communicate with me.*

J · - - -   *I am on fire and have dangerous cargo on board: keep well clear of me.*

K - · -   *I wish to communicate with you.*

L . _ . .   *You should stop your vessel instantly.*

O - - -   *Man overboard.*

Q - - · -   *My vessel is healthy and I request free practique.*

T -   *Keep clear of me; I am engaged in pair trawling.*

U . . _   *You are running into danger.*

V . . . _   *I require assistance.*

W . _ _   *I require medical assistance.*

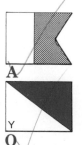
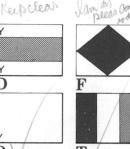
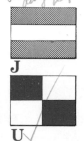

VHF PROCEDURES

1. **ALWAYS LISTEN FOR 30 SECS BEFORE TRANSMITTING** so you do not interrupt a distress call or someone already using that channel.
2. **THINK BEFORE TRANSMITTING** if you are uncertain, write your message down and simply read it out. This will avoid long pauses.

TO MAKE A CALL TO COASTAL RADIO STATION (DISTRESS ON PAGE 56)

1. Select one of its working channels (listed in almanacs) *NOT CH16*.
2. Reduce background noise with VOLUME and SQUELCH controls.
3. LISTEN — if you here voice or 'pips', try later or another channel.
4. Press TRANSMIT BUTTON on microphone if silent.
5. IDENTIFY STATION CALLED ONCE eg. *"NITON RADIO"*
6. Identify calling station TWICE eg. *"This is Yacht Nelson, Yacht Nelson, Mike, November, Delta, Lima, Zulu"*
7. Invite a reply *"Over"*.
8. Release TRANSMIT BUTTON
9. LISTEN — If you hear 'pips' you are connected so wait for a reply.

TO CALL INTERSHIP

Unless you have made prior arrangements select CH16
Repeat the above procedure (but there will be no 'pips')
"Yacht Emma — This is Yacht Nelson, Yacht Nelson — Over"

The VESSEL CALLED then nominates an intership channel.
"Yacht Nelson — This is Yacht Emma — channel 26 — over"

THE MAXIMUM LENGTH OF A NONE DISTRESS CALL ON CH16 IS 1 MIN.

KEEP YOUR MESSAGE SHORT AND FINISH WITH *"OUT"* MAKE SURE THE TRANSMIT BUTTON IS NOT JAMMED ON AS THIS CAN BLOCK RADIO WORKING ON THAT CHANNEL FOR HUNDREDS OF SQUARE MILES.

COASTGUARD can be contacted on CH16 for any safety reasons including a radio check.
HARBOURS on a working channel or CH16.
U.K. MARINAS on channel M.

PHONETIC ALPHABET

It is sometimes necessary to spell out yacht names, call signs, abreviations and words and the following table conforms to international agreement:

LETTER	WORD	HOW SAID (underlined syllables to be emphasised)			
A	Alfa	ALFAH	N	November	NOVEMBER
B	Bravo	BRAHVOH	O	Oscar	OSSCAH
C	Charlie	CHARLEE	P	Papa	PAHPAH
D	Delta	DELLTAH	Q	Quebec	KEHBECK
E	Echo	ECKOH	R	Romeo	ROWMEOH
F	Foxtrot	FOXSTROT	S	Sierra	SEEAIRRAH
G	Golf	GOLF	T	Tango	TANGGO
H	Hotel	HOTELL	U	Uniform	YOUNEEFORM
I	India	INDEEAH	V	Victor	VIKTAH
J	Juliett	JEWLEEETT	W	Whiskey	WISSKEY
K	Kilo	KEYLOH	X	X-ray	ECKSRAY
L	Lima	LEEMAH	Y	Yankee	YANGKEY
M	Mike	MIKE	Z	Zulu	ZOOLOO

A VHF RADIO OPERATORS CERTIFICATE IS NEEDED TO USE A RADIO LEGALLY

PASSAGE PLANNING

A. OVERALL PLANNING

Look at entire passage on small scale chart.

Identify: Best route to make best use of tidal streams and available navaids.

Large scale charts for passage and possible diversion ports.

Shipping lanes and Traffic Separation Schemes.

Sunrise and sunset times (for light identification) Soundings which might give progress check.

Draft outline plan, note distance and likely passage time.

B. TIDES AND TIDAL STREAMS

Note: times and heights of HW and LW at departure and destination.

Time of HW and range at reference point for tidal atlas and tidal diamonds.

Identify limiting depths and fast streams causing "tidal gates", correcting plan as necessary.

C. NAVAIDS

Visibility of lights. Ranges of radiobeacons.

Amend plan as necessary to optimise use.

D. DETAILED PLAN

1. PILOTAGE FOR DEPARTURE PORT, DESTINATION AND POSSIBLE DIVERSION PORTS.

Study large scale charts and sailing directions.

2. OPEN SEA PASSAGES   Tracks, courses to steer, methods of navigation.

3. DANGERS   Distance off to pass, clearing lines.

4. SHIPPING LANES   Cross at right angles?

5. DIVERSION PORTS   Good shelter? Tidal or other restrictions.

6. FUEL   Gals/hour — passage time — 20% reserve.

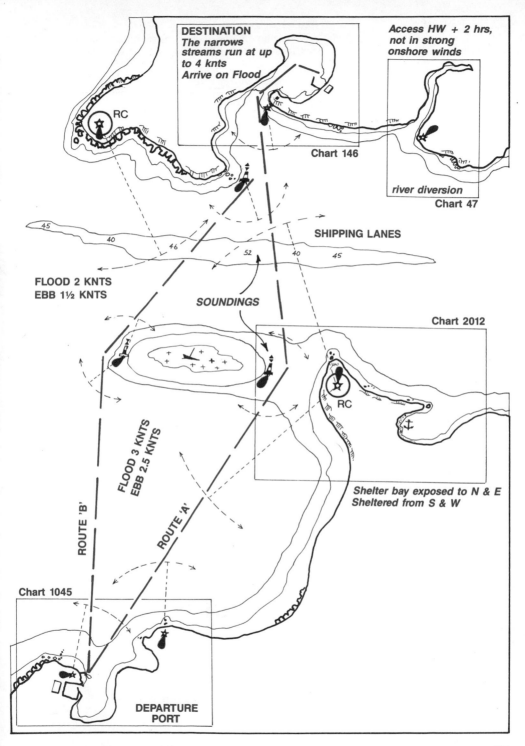

DESTINATION
The narrows
streams run at up
to 4 knts
Arrive on Flood

RC

Access HW + 2 hrs,
not in strong
onshore winds

Chart 146

river diversion
Chart 47

45
40
46
52
40
45

SHIPPING LANES

FLOOD 2 KNTS
EBB 1½ KNTS

SOUNDINGS

Chart 2012

RC

FLOOD 3 KNTS
EBB 2.5 KNTS

Shelter bay exposed to N & E
Sheltered from S & W

ROUTE 'B'

ROUTE 'A'

Chart 1045

DEPARTURE
PORT

LOG BOOKS

An accurate record of navigational information should be kept in some form of note book or log book. This lets the navigator check back when his position in in doubt.

TIME G.M.T.	LOG	COMPASS COURSE STEERED	ESTIMATED LEEWAY	WIND DIR/STR	BARO METER	REMARKS
9.25	—	—	—	SW/4	1012	SLIPPED MOORING UNDER ENGINE
9.58	121.4	—	—	"	"	FAIRWAY BY. FULL MAIN No1 JIB — COURSE 180°(c)
10.35	123.7	182°	5°	SW/5	"	WIND INCREASED 1 SLAB IN MAIN

If you have DECCA or LORAN you need to log their readings.

TIME GMT	SHIPS POSITION LAT	LONG	WPT NO.	WAYPOINT POSITION LAT	LONG	WAYPOINT BRG. T.M.C.	DIST.	VAR.	DEV.	COURSE MADE GOOD	SPEED MADE GOOD